Edited by
Chris Coates
Jonathan How
Lee Jones
William Morris
Andy Wood

DIGGERS AND DREAMERS PUBLICATIONS

©
Diggers & Dreamers
Publications
1995

First published
1995
D&D Publications
PO Box 1808
Winslow
Buckinghamshire
MK18 3RN

ISBN
0 9514945 3 8
Paperback

Distribution
Edge of Time Ltd
PO Box 1808
Winslow
Buckinghamshire
MK18 3RN
Printing (contents)
Greenwood Recycled
Printing
Lakeside
off Warehouse Hill
Marsden
Huddersfield
HD7 6AE
(01484) 844841
Printing (cover)
Buckingham Colour Press
Riverside Works
Bridge Street
Buckingham
MK18 1EN
(01280) 824000
Typesetting and Layout
Jonathan How
PO Box 1808
Winslow
Buckinghamshire
MK18 3RN

Cover photograph: Communards from all over Britain gather at the 1994 Inter-Communities Volleyball Tournament held at Redfield. Photograph by Jonathan How

Contents

Preface

Afeature article about communes in *Good Housekeeping*, whole colour supplements turned over to alternative lifestyles, *Blue Peter* presented from a commune! Is the world turned upside down, or are we seeing the coming of age of the counter-culture? As we raise our sights towards the millenium are we seeing a swing back towards communalistic values - crushed during the Thatcherite years - that will be an antidote to the apocalyptic doom mongering of the likes of the Japanese Oum cult? We at *Diggers and Dreamers* would hope so.

> *Now I don't have any doubts that we've gone too far in an individualistic direction, that we've lost too many of the valuable aspects of a more co-operative way of living ... Everywhere traditional groupings are breaking up, and traditional communal cultures being discarded. The level of tension and anxiety is rising, and that always increases the tendency for people to take the attitude we used to describe as 'I'm alright Jack, pull up the ladder'. So, Doctor, how can we reverse this tendency towards greater individualism, and get back to a healthier balance?*
>
> John Cleese
> *LIFE and how to survive it.*

During the last couple of years interest in communal living has been on the increase. *Diggers & Dreamers 94/95* sold out and there was a regular stream of stories and reports on communes in the press, most of them positive. Now whether this is a trend or just media hype is hard to tell, but whatever it is we hope that this book will contribute to the continuing success and ongoing debate. We invite you to join us on the journey and adventure that is communal living.

Acknowledgements: Thank you to all the communities, housing co-ops and other organisations that have responded to our requests for information; and to the many authors who have so admirably come up with the goods. We're indebted to Medusa who keyed in a lot of the entries and to the optical character reader that did the rest! We've been all over the place for our meetings in the last two years, so thank you to everyone at Crabapple; People in Common; Birchwood; Braziers and Redfield for being such friendly and interesting hosts. Thanks also to those readers who responded to our survey, your questionnaires provided much food for thought.

The Value of Art to Community

CATRIONA STAMP

Some say that a community is the ideal place for an artist to live

while others maintain that an artistic temperament is

incompatible with communitarian ideals.

As an artist who has lived in community for many years I wanted to look at what art could contribute to a community and to understand why I had not been very successful at introducing my art to the people I lived with. I

The photograph on page 5 shows the Clachanpluck Band at Laurieston Hall. Photograph by Alice.

contacted many communities but in the end only visited a few, mainly Findhorn Foundation (FF), Laurieston Hall (LH) and Twin Oaks. Even so the amount of material is too great for me to do it justice in this article. I would like to thank everyone who took the time to answer my questions whether they have been quoted or not. Everyone helped in increasing my understanding. Throughout my research I used the term 'art' to refer to the widest range possible of creative behaviour, and included art and craft, whether lasting or temporary, classic or folk, but in practice what I covered was mainly visual art, dance, music, theatre, and pottery.

The contribution which art may make to a community is hard to measure, and so it may often be undervalued by the group, particularly as a reflection also of the attitudes towards art found in Western society, where it is seen as the cream on top, not something socially useful. I believe that art, in my definition, is indispensible, and plays a part in producing social cohesion, as well as forming an outlet for critique, leading to change. However I will be happy if in this article I manage to show that art is socially useful.

Art can be one factor which holds people together in a community. For some it can be the most important factor, while others prefer meetings, socialising or working together as a way of promoting group bonding. I am not going to try to assess the relative importance of these factors, but concentrate on how art may enhance group functioning.

During Work
Sometimes it is used consciously during work time, to promote integration at a deeper level. Barbara Swetina used her music skills in the kitchen at Findhorn Foundation "as a tool to allow the group to form and bond," to make a good experience of a stressful job, by focussing on group singing, using short mantra-style songs from many cultures which could be learnt quickly and the benefit of harmony easily reached. Clive Kitson led

groups of people in different work departments at Findhorn Foundation to make joint pictures of their work. He saw this as "a group experience, using the vehicle of art for people to relate to each other in a different way," and to initiate "group process and insight," for the same dynamics operated in miniature, and yet could be more readily observed and worked with on this level.

"In my work I bring the spirit of creativity, fun and exploration into mundane tasks ... it is not necessary to be as efficient as possible, I need work to be nurturing and fulfilling as well, and to put passion and heart into it."

At Laurieston commitment and morale is increased at the start and end of Maintenance Weeks by a Tour of Works, which incorporates "a parade, with music, drumming and applause at each site, - to get a sense of what has been achieved " (Gilly Fordham)

Participative Art
Other members of community value the use of art on a participative level. Then its main value is as a way to play together, to relax, to communicate in ways which are different from the day to day. In this way it can counterbalance the emphasis on efficiency and reality which is so necessary for the functioning of communities, and it can be energizing, nurturing and restorative, and can open people to ways of being and behaving with each other which break with personal norms and the cultural norms of their community.

Richard Langley (LH). "I have a natural tendency to wander in a serious, get-things-done mode, and try and fit it all in. [Art events] break me out of that mode ... [they are] primarily for me to be in a dif-

> "It's important for me to do unexpected things that prove I'm not a boring old fart. It changes my view of me, and others' view of me, and gets me out of grumpy work mode."
> Patrick Upton
> Laurieston Hall

ferent space with people than normal ... it is nice to be able to make things that don't have permanence and to play with others.

Phil (LH) reflects on the benefit which the group as a whole can derive from the sharing involved in participative art and the risks to a community if life becomes increasingly privatised.

Phil (LH) "Once you start you know you'll get a huge buzz ... If you don't do this [art, celebration] with others here, you start looking outwards ... it is dangerous not to do it ... the private part of our lives is getting richer and more comfortable faster than the communal side. Some people are aware of it, but there is no energy coming in to counteract it ... the importance of talking to each other in different ways can't be emphasized enough ... Lots of folks here are very conventional, and don't like, say, to hold hands before a meeting or to change places during it. It is good in performances because this stuff can be done there."

It is perhaps more usual for participative art to reinforce the cultural norms of the community, which seems to be the case with the Taizé singing at Findhorn Foundation. Taizé is a Christian ecumenical community in France where Barbara Swetina learnt religious rounds and songs, which she brought back to her own community. Now it is possible to sing these songs every morning at the Nature Sanctuary, and every Sunday at Minton House.

Barbara Swetina says that, "prayers deepen when we sing ... it's to do with the ability to open to divine love, the unlimited source, to give and to receive. It opens the heart channel, to have energy for others. It is a form of group alchemy." Kate O'Connell says, "Taizé is my church. Singing puts me directly into the experience of being one with everything."

Art offers people the chance to form different groups from those of work or residence, and is particularly important in this regard when the community is large and/or co-op based so that opportunities to meet some people in the group will be limited. Even large communities are limited in size and opportunities compared with large towns and cities that most people in Britain are used to. A surprisingly wide pool is needed to provide deep friendships. While some friends are necessary for emotional survival in a community, being friends with everyone is extremely unlikely as joining is often based instead on shared aims. Within this situation art can provide another way of bridging the gap and easing communication with people whose attitudes or ways of being in daily life are less compatible.

Patrick Upton (LH). "We are a co-op with a variety of set-ups. The actual overlapping goes on in the functions we create such as woodtrips, music and dance. This is less entrenching - there is a bonus from them all overlapping, with some people from each group. If by chance one activity was occupied by people perceived as powerful in the main group that could lead to problems ... friendship in community is the level most missed out. We are more like family than friends, so we connect through social events, especially those which are activity-based."

As Entertainment
Some art in communities is not just participative, but from time to time is used to provide entertainment, so that the community is divided into performers and audience. As entertainment, it may often be appreciated as being free from commercial values, validating individuals' skills and contributions, but I think it is most valued when it also functions at a deeper level of meaning. At this level it holds up a mirror to the community, emphasizing the common language and belief systems and allowing people to see in what ways they are failing to live up to their goals, often using humour to make the point but avoid the hurt of direct criticism.

Several people talked of the way 'sharings' work at the Findhorn Community. Brian Nobbs, Focaliser of the Pottery Studio (FF): "They are skits, not psychodrama, and are a gentle voice of criticism, when it can be presented with humour to soften the harshness of criticism." Sharon Took-Zozaya and Buffy Hart in discussion talked about the early days of the Findhorn Community, when skits were regular events on a Friday night encouraged by Peter Caddy as a form of community building, for art was seen as one of the keys to binding people together so that they would be more inclined to hold the vision.

John Wheeler (LH), made the point that the use of humour as a mirror does not always avoid hurt, however unintentional and deeply regretted. "There is an element of the court jester or fool, which I was not aware of at first, but I like the idea that I introduce a bit of that here. I don't do it as well as a heyoka - that is a far distant ideal ... One memorable occasion when I took the mick and did a sketch on circle dance - that was quite disruptive - it caused big waves - it upset one person who thought the piss was being taken out of them - it wasn't meant personally - and I'm really sorry about that."

> "I'll only really appreciate circle dance when I've left, but it can be a lifesaver if I feel sick in my soul - it has often felt restorative."
>
> John Wheeler
> Laurieston Hall

Alice (LH), finds that her photographs act as a mirror for people, which enables them to see themselves in a new way, often in relationship to other people or in a group rather than as individuals. She sees one important function of her photography as that of recording the group's own history.

Brian Nobbs (FF) is not only a potter but also paints and draws his vision of the tree and plant devas. This connects with the philosophy of Findhorn Foundation, that every member needs to have a serious commitment to searching for the ultimate reality in their existence, to aligning themselves with that overall transpersonal will." For some, like

Brian, this means recognizing the interpenetrating worlds of other spirits.

The entertainment itself comes in different forms; celebrations for particular events, such as birthdays of individuals or the community, or points in the year's cycle and economic life of the community, or may be the flowering of a creative phase by a group of members which they wish to share with the rest of the community."

The contributions which art can make to these events varies considerably in type and extent, from making a personal contribution such as a sculptural birthday cake or a giant three-dimensional birthday card, to sharing skills by leading workshops and enabling everyone to make a themed contribution such as when Annie (LH) led workshops in lantern making in preparation for Alice's fiftieth birthday. It can give chances for people who think of themselves as non-artists to contribute by decorating spaces and transforming the everyday environment, by joining in with wassailing songs, being the bonfire lighter, being part of processions etc. I am partic-

A giant model of Laurieston Hall filled with sweets, made by the author to celebrate the community's 20th birthday

ularly fascinated by the development in communities of formats which encourage greater participation.

There are two formats which lend themselves well to the skill pools generally available in communities: tableaux and cabarets. Neither of these requires a high level of skill or interest in a particular limited field, in comparison with for example, a musical, which requires some acting and musical ability from all involved. For tableaux and cabarets access is only limited by a degree of courage in appearing before an audience and imagination in preparing the act. Participants can choose their best artistic skill, appearing solo or with a group, and are more in control of what they do, rather than under stage director's orders.

Nonetheless, some communities are able to create full-scale productions at certain points in their history due, I think, to the particular combinations of people available. Twin Oaks has written and performed several musicals, and Laurieston Hall has the Clachenpluck Band and three pantos to its credit, though it is interesting to note that the first panto was held at the Hall, the next in the village, and the third included local people in the performance.

Earlier on I referred to the way art can emphasize the common language and belief system of the community, and Twin Oaks has provided some good examples of that. Many of the buildings, and most of the work duties were referred to by initials, and in my three week visit I remained mystified not only by reality, but also by the cabaret adaptation of the Twelve Days of Christmas, in which numerous jobs were given out daily, such as KP3, perhaps some reference to kitchen work. The song had people screaming with laughter, probably also as a result of the recogition of how hard members have to work, and of the necessity for the work to be what the community needs and not always what each person likes to do most.

The Wizard of Iz, an adaptation by Lesley of Twin Oaks, makes references to the initialling habit.

Rut: "Elmer, uh, I hate to um ... say it but, it kinda sorta sounds like you're um, pressure trading, just to ... um remind you about the haggling and fair trade agreement, HAFTA.' (Points to sign that says Remember, you HAFTA?)

Dottie: "She said there was some rule about C4, Contributing Citizens Capitulate to Co-operate ..."

There is also the language and nomenclature used which reflects on the belief system, whether the language is in actual everyday use or not, eg "economical living cluster", the "radically equal Communikins", "unearned privilege", the "Identical Guild" and "Equality League", "Barterville" and "Amoral City", "all negative and no positive feedback".

The witches are transformed into those scourges of communal life, "The Itch of the Yeast" and "The Lousy Itch of the Vest", and the heroine's three companions have vices appropriate to Twin Oaks value system: ScaredyCo, being too scared to find out or attempt things: Packrat, never being satisfied - indiscriminatingly wanting more stuff; and Cow, who is an adversarial, uncooperative, black and white thinker.

> "I am particularly fascinated by the development in communities of formats which encourage greater participation."

One of the high points in the musical from the point of view of providing a mirror, which was much appreciated by the audience, occurs in the confrontation between Dottie and The Lousy Itch of the Vest - Dottie: "We've come such a long way and its been such a long process already ..." (Wild peel of laughter from Lousy Itch).

Itch: "You call that *long*? Why you don't know how long a process can be." Evil laugh.

Twin Oakers are in no doubt about how long the process of decision-making can take, much to everyone's frustration, even if it does lead to better decisions.

Production of such major works requires dedication and commitment from all concerned, but the inspiration usually comes from one person, and this can be more draining than the rest of the community recognises, even when they appreciate the result both for community entertainment and individual development.

At Laurieston Hall, John Luff has been the main inspiration behind making music such an important part of the community that at least half the members are directly involved in group music making, though others perform alone or outside the community. (And he was drawn to Laurieston because they had a tradition of circle dance - mainly due to Alice Simpson - which he hoped to be able to build on.)

John had his own personal reasons for starting the Clackenpluck Band, which plays circle and folk dance music and I think his reasons and his approach were crucial to the on-going success of muslc at Laurieston. He enjoyed playing in a small band and wanted to pass that pleasure on to others including those with little or no musical experience. He was mindful of the encouragement he had recieved when he first started in a band and wanted, in a way, to repay that debt. Once the band was successfully established he began to take on board how that might effect the rest of the community

"I didn't want to cause a division in the community and was anxious that it didn't develop into a mystique."

So over the five years he has lived there he has set up music groups to cover other interests and needs, and was particularly pleased that several people who were the mainstays of the Clackenpluck Band had not been able to play music at the start as this helped break down the mystique. He was already aware of the advantages that music has for a community: "Music is more interesting when done with other people. Music is a sharing thing." However for Laurieston Hall the focus that music has provided has been particularly beneficial in winter as there is an inclination for people to go into social hibernation when the conference season is over. "The different groups" (small recorder band, wind band, Balkan choir, shape note singing, beginners' band) lead to more cohesion in the community which is especially important in winter. If you are not careful you don't see people in winter. This gets us together."

What he could not foresee was how important learning music was to be in terms of people's personal development. "The Beginners' Recorders seemed like a simple matter of people being able to learn music. I hadn't appreciated that because they were adults it would be a big deal. All children play recorders at school so it must be easy" (ironic tone of voice). "It creates a crisis of confidence. I wasn't expecting it. I had to encourage people not to drop out. It became for some people important in a way I never imagined because of the sense of achievement."

As well as growth in confidence in playing and performing in public, some individuals can be inspired by such an experience to make a career in the arts. This happened to Allie as a result of John's initiatives. "I started a choir although I'm not a singer and Allie asked to take a few sessions. I realised she had more ability at that than I did, so I asked would she take over the choir. Then she found that is what she wanted to do." So she left the community to pursue that dream successfully.

... art is one way through which the barriers of prejudice and value differences can be broken down, by sharing enthusiasms and making personal links.

Music and movement at Findhorn - a bridge to the local community

Relationship to the Community

So far I have looked at the internal workings of communities, but the relationship to the local people is also important, and art is one way through which the barriers of prejudice and value differences can be broken down, by sharing enthusiasms and making personal links. Members of a community can initiate this process, by teaching, by leading events such as ceilidhs in town or music sessions in the local pub or being the motivating force behind them, or by inviting local residents to events at the community such as fire festivals.

Reaching out to the local people through teaching was a frequent theme for artists living at or near the Findhorn Foundation, while the other methods were referred to more often by members of Laurieston Hall, though each community uses both.

The artists in and around the Findhorn Foundation form a supportive community for each other. They have decided to produce a directory, similar to the one the healers have, to spell out how many hours work is done, how many people benefit, and what links are formed with the local region, as a way of supporting their request for recognition. Many of them run classes locally or at the Findhorn Foundation, for which they have produced a joint brochure, offering in the Winter Season 1994-1995 four painting classes, life, beginner's, children's and primal, a pottery class, a weaving class, a recorder group, and three dance classes - circle, devotional and contemporary.

Randy Klinger, who focalises the Art Sanctuary and who runs two of the art classes, spoke of how it formed a bridge to the local community and how it brings together, for example, a gardener, a classics master, and someone from the RAF. Car pooling has developed among some members of his class. Those who come value what he offers to the extent of travelling regularly from Elgin, Gordonstoun and Inverness, a radius of up to 40 miles. For those whose work is isolated, painting at a class can be a social event and the discussions are free-ranging, covering topics such as ghosts or dreams. Randy believes that this adds to the integration of the group and aids their concentration. He deliberately avoids spiritual matters, believing that to be a private matter.

Kate O'Connell has also discovered that toning down the specialised language helped draw in more local people. "I drew up a poster for some voice workshops and cut out the jargon words. The librarian putting it up looked at it and said, 'I'll come'. It makes it more accessible, and doesn't make any promises."

Dave Till, focaliser/administrator for the Universal Hall, reflected on the position of The Foundation as an implanted community, which could be seen to pose a threat to the local people in all sorts of ways right down to taking over the village's name. He feels that art reduces some of these tensions. One of the chief local critics of The Foundation goes to an art class taught by one of the community's artists, so that social contact is made and some prejudices can be dissolved. His main challenge at the minute is to get the Universal Hall more used than it is, but he still feels that it is a success to run a theatre in that area with no local urban population to draw on. He is aware that it is still hard for people to make the first step and come through the gate, but in a region where the provision for art is scarce, there is a big incentive for people to overcome their suspicions.

"We put on a son et lumière about the history of Redfield and over 200 people came. We gained a lot of friends that evening"

Jonathan How

Redfield

Celebrations do not need to be limited to members, but can benefit from drawing in people from the local community. At events such as a community's twenty-fifth birthday party, it may be important to recognise in some way the impact that the community has had upon a small rural population. At other times members may find that what they want to celebrate can only draw enough support if the wider community is invited. This can initially feel disappointing, but can also be experienced as an opening up to others.

Kate O'Connell asked herself in the past, "Why organise an equinox celebration, if it's not 'family'?" Her answer? "Now whoever we dance with is our community." So as a community grows in confidence in itself, it can reach out to the local community through art as well as in other ways, and share skills and imagination in ways which range from the ordinary evening class with its own special flavour, to the strange and wacky - such as the fire festivals at Laurieston Hall.

This small survey has made me realise that the value of art to a community depends on various factors:
- whether the skills and interests of resident artists support and are consistent with the aims and philosophy of the group,
- on the ability of artists to work with and communicate with others through their art.

I have found that art can be used in many different ways, sometimes consciously, which most often happens when art is used to enhance work. On the whole, though, people take part in art events in a less conscious way, because it adds to their lives in terms of enjoyment, energy, socialising, sense of harmony or commitment, whether they are participating or being an audience. But art doesn't just happen. I came away from my interviews with a sense of the immense amount of work put in by any artist who acts as a focus or initiator, however much the artist also gains personally. It is a recognition of this from their community which artists need, to get support and avoid burn-out, and also to guide them in how to integrate their own personal artistic needs with those of the community.

My house

a poem by Rosie Kentwood of Rainbow

I love to live near my friends,
The fun and laughter never ends.
We live together
And squash up tight
And sleep in comfort every night.
We live together with people that we know
And strangers that come and go.
The strangers don't do us any harm,
Living here is one big charm.

Ken Chiba, artist in residence at Braziers, spoke of how important he thought it was that he had lived at Braziers as an ordinary member first, so that he had insight into the community to help him to juggle with the inevitable conflict over time.

As an artist myself, I have a feeling that even a full-time artist never has enough time for all the ideas. I have gained from these interviews an understanding of the importance of balancing what I gain from the community against what I can give back that will be welcome, rather than simply what I can produce that satisfies my own individual artistic needs.

Catriona Stamp was born in 1950. She joined Laurieston hall in 1974 and moved to People in Common in 1982. She is interested in nearly everything, from shamanism to quantum physics, and passionate about art, therapy (both as client and counsellor) and how to effect useful change in society.

Taking our Responsibilities Seriously

BOB FROMER

Some communities live by rules. Others die by them ("I don't care

what the damned rota says, I'm not taking the pig slops out on

Wednesdays!" "Oh yes you are!" "Fuck you!" "I'm off!").

A t Birchwood, we pride ourselves on the fact that we don't have any written rules at all - much like those people who take pride in the fact that Britain doesn't have a written Constitution or Bill of Rights! And only two things are mandated by rota: you must cook every now and again, and twice a year you must sign up to do the monthly staples shop. Otherwise, freedom (dare one say anarchy?) rules!

Of course, we do have a cleaning rota as well, but no one takes that seriously so it doesn't really count. And it lets us bring the topic of cleaning up two or three times a year at feelings meetings, which provides a useful form of catharsis ("The house is a pigsty!" "Well, whose fault is that, then!?" "Actually, you know, pigs are very clean!" "Pedant!" "Animal!").

On the other hand, we have conducted two very scary exercises over the past few years, the results of which were so disturbing that they have been hidden away in a nondescript folder in the corner of a very dark cupboard and are referred to only in whispers (if at all). The first exercise, which was meant to be light-hearted, was to compile a list of all the "unwritten rules" by which we at Birchwood imagine we conduct our lives. Accordingly, an A4 sheet of paper was circulated (one would surely be sufficient!) and everyone was encouraged to write down those few bits of hallowed custom and practice which might occur to them.

Some of the more obvious ones went down first:

• Thou shalt not serve heavily garlicked meals when the teenagers are going out afterwards!

• Thou shalt not plan last-minute camping trips in the Scottish Highlands on weekends when prospective new members are coming.

• Thou shalt not sleep with other members' partners (this rule has been broken only once in the past ten years, by a long-stay visitor, and the result was the destruction of a nuclear family and the eventual loss of four members, two of them well under the age of consent, thus proving one of two things: the wisdom of the rule or the fact that a doomed relationship will always find a way to self-destruct!).

But when the list reached 113, with enough pages to fill a small ring-binder, we began to sense that perhaps we were in trouble. Could it be that our carefree and unfettered lives were in fact governed by enough ingrained rituals to fill the Egyptian Book of the Dead?

Inevitably, trouble flared one winter's night over Rule Number 63, one of the more obscure injunctions in the manual. This read something like: *With regard to use and operation of the communal television and video, television watching in real time and video recording shall both take precedence over video watching.*

"But I was bored!", said the newish member who had deactivated a programmed recording in order to watch a Billy Connolly video. "It was Friday night, everyone else had gone out and all the programmes on television were crap! I don't understand why recording has precedence over watching, anyway! Why can't I watch a video when I want to!?"

A collective shudder went through the room as it simultaneously occurred to all the old-timers that the reason why we never had written rules, only unwritten ones, was precisely so that this kind of confrontation could never occur, and that by writing rules down (even in jest), we had opened a Pandora's Box that could destroy us all.

We had opened a Pandora's Box that could destroy us all

So that list has never been seen again and rumour has it that it was donated to the space mission designed to send human artefacts on a journey to Alpha Centauri in the extremely optimistic hope that intelligent life elsewhere in the universe might be interested.

A couple of years later, however, when collective sensibilities had recovered, we were foolhardy enough to embark on a second and similar exercise: namely, to make a list of all those communal tasks and responsibilities that were *not* mandated by rota, but which nevertheless seemed to get accomplished, as if by the spirit of the beehive. If anything, this exercise touched on something even more fundamental than the unwritten rules: namely, our collective trust that all necessary things will eventually get done and that each individual, in one way or another, will do her or his share.

This trust obviates the need for any of us to consider exactly who is doing what and eliminates those destructively loaded issues about whether X is doing more than Y or whether Z is doing enough. Those sorts of questions will tear a community apart more quickly than anything else except sex and money, and it's one of our genuine successes that they hardly ever get raised,

Two or three years ago, a misguided newish member began to lay on moral pressure about the kitchen garden: "Well, I think everyone ought to put in some time up there; it's not fair that just a few of us are doing it all!" The silence that greeted this remark was palpable, the subject was never raised again, and the garden continues to supplement (and deliciously, too!) the Cash-and-Carry, thanks to the efforts of those people - about half of us - who actually like gardening.

Because of all this, we felt that putting communal responsibilities down on paper might hold fewer nasty surprises than the unwritten rules. But once again, we were stunned by the sheer volume of things that need to be done (and that someone invariably does) to keep our household ticking over. This time, we quit when the list reached 89, though there was a feeling that this was far from exhaustive. Again, there were obvious responsibilities:

- Paying house bills.
- Taking out the compost.
- Mowing the lawns.
- Cutting and stacking logs.
- Taking bottles, cans etc to the recycling centre.

And then there were less obvious tasks that nevertheless make a major contribution to general happiness and well-being:
- Lighting the wood stove in the television room on winter afternoons for (a) children watching kids' programmes before supper and (b) adults watching afterwards.
- Feeding the largely-ignored communal fish.
- Re-painting the initials on the chalkboard in the kitchen when members arrive or depart (these initials are there as an aid to cooks in calculating how many people are in for supper and what they will or won't eat).
- Putting the milk in the fridge and separating out the red, blue, silver and gold-top for ease of access.
- Locking up doors and windows at night.
- Fetching the newspaper from the mailbox at the front gate, preferably before lunch, so that those at home for lunchtime can read it.

- Keeping the events board in the back hall up to date by removing posters for last week's lecture on permaculture and putting up the notice about next month's seminar on Cystitis in Rural Britain.
- Refilling the paper roll in the telephone logger.
- Making up bedrooms for visitors - including the traditional vase of flowers!
- Looking after equipment guarantees, repair contracts etc,.
- Updating the computer rents programme.
- Watering the communal indoor plants.
- Making jam and marmalade.
- Turning off redundant lights.
- And - cleaning out the bio-digester!

There was one item on the list, however, which suddenly gave us pause. Under Number 39, someone had written:

- Spend time with people in the community.

What? Really? Was this a communal responsibility? With all our systems working so well, and with everything managing somehow to get done (even Number 33: "Making Bread" and Number 65: "Making Yogurt", was it really necessary for us actually to spend *time* with each other? I mean, didn't we have supper together every evening? Wasn't that enough?

Once again, a list compiled in all innocence seemed to be creating a yawning chasm under our feet, an abyss into which we dared not look, lest we be consumed; lest (and this was far worse) the pattern of our individual lives might face disruption. So this list, too, was consigned to the inner darkness of the folder in the cupboard, the folder that no one can ever quite manage to find.

And we've all lived quite happily ever since!

Bob Fromer is an American who has lived communally since 1972. First in London, then at Blue Frog House in Kington, Herefordshire. Since 1984 he has been at Birchwood Hall.

Chris Coates asks: Who Killed Communes Network?
... and then confesses

The Network is Dead ... Long Live the Network!

News may have reached you, on the grapevine, of the 'scandalous' demise of Communes Network. Conceived on 15/16 February 1975 at the Gorilla Family in Birmingham as an inter-commune-self-help group (see D&D 92/93 for a detailed history of the early years of CN) it lasted nearly twenty years.

But it had lost its way long before that. Slowly dwindling in subscriptions so that in the end it was insolvent - it owed more issues to subscribers than it had money to produce.

Finding it harder and harder to find groups willing to do the editorial work, the magazine ended up being put out by an ever smaller circle of communities. Increasingly the magazine was made up of articles, news, bits and pieces written by the editorial community and people from outside communities. Becoming in some cases no more than an advert for the editorial community with not much of the mutual inter-commune self-help that was the vision of the founders. In fact its relevance to communities was, in the end, such that only 15 subscribed to it.

The so-called "Readers' Meetings" were notable for their lack of commune members attending and from my recollection were taken up by white male intellectuals who didn't live in communes pontificating about what we, who did, 'ought' to be doing.

So the writing was on the communal laundry wall. And I admit it, I read it, I saw the opportunity, I did it ..."I", said the sparrow, "with my bow and arrow, I killed off Communes Network." This is not my defence, more a brief post-mortem. In the end the D&D editorial group had de facto become Communes Network - in the absence of anyone else we were answering the mail, and with increasing gaps between editions of CN (and the knowledge that CN was insolvent) we were becoming more and more embarrassed at taking people's subscription money under, what seemed to be, false pretences.

So at the 1994 Community Volleyball Games I called a meeting to "officially" wind up the Network. I know that some people have questioned whether this was an appropriate place to do it but it was, after all, the largest gathering of people from communities in ten years. Reactions at the meeting ranged from "Communes What? ... never heard of it", "I thought it finished years ago!" to a feeling of sadness for the passing of a once loved friend ...

Subscribers were either sent their money back or a copy of D&D; it was agreed that D&D Publications would take on the production of a "Places needing People" sheet (updated every six months) which would be included with mail-order sales of the book.

Chris from Redfield agreed to see what interest there was in an inter-communities news sheet and found practically zzzzilch. Despite this Lifespan are attempting to continue CN as a newsletter for communities - contact them for further info.

The Virtual Communes Network

Even members of the remotest rural commune will have heard of the Internet. The much hyped harbinger of the "New-information Age". What you may not know is that the Internet was developed by members of the counter-culture in west coast America and in particular people involved in the Whole Earth Catalogue and from the Tennessee Farm Commune (for the full details of this intriguing story see: "The Virtual Community: Home-steading on the electronic frontier by Howard Rheingold).

In this country (hell there are no countries in cyberspace!) communities are starting to use the Internet to communicate. Findhorn already has a conference on GreenNet and a World Wide Web home page. Other communities receive visitor letters by e-mail and D&D orders are now processed using an electronic communications.

Now imagine for a moment Communes Network on the Internet ... on second thoughts get a modem and join it.

Introducing: Diggers & Dreamers Millenium Celebration Scheme - The Communal Living Archive Project

Diggers & Dreamers has covered the history of communities from the 1800s to the 1950s. Now faced with covering the 1960s & 70s and not wanting to become persona non grata in every community in the country, we will not be attempting to write a definitive history of communes in the sixties & seventies. Instead we are planning an oral history project to cover the period. We hope to carry out the project over the next four years with the aim of bringing out a book and possibly tapes/ CDs/ CD-ROMs to coincide with D&D 2000/2001. The idea is to interview a wide cross section of people involved in communes during 60s/70s - founder members/ visitors/ families/ neigh-bours about a whole range of issues and subjects connected to communal living. The tapes would then be archived at either the Commonweal Collection at Bradford University/ the Working Class Library in Salford or at the National Sound Archive. We would also hope to set up an archive for photos and literature from the period. If you would be willing to be interviewed, or have any literature/ photos that you would be willing to donate to the Archive or lend for copying then please contact us via D&D.

Towards Intentional Community

BILL SMALE

An Antipodean look at the opportunities of generational change.

Mandala, in South East Queensland, Australia, my home for two decades, is attempting a transformation from an unfocussed group of land sharers, into an intentional community. In this piece, I tell only part of the story: the conditions which made some political and organisational changes possible, the nature of those changes, and the new possibilities they have engendered. Not described: is the painstaking, continuing work done on group and interpersonal dynamics. Not yet known: is how our intentional community will develop, in its new complexity, synergy, and focus on change. I write *of* rather than *for* my community in this article.

A History
Mandala is typical of many of the Australian rural, secular communities which formed in the early to mid seventies. Such communities were influenced by often contradictory beliefs and myths, such as: 'Age of Aquarius', tribal, feel-good dreamings - the 'politics of ecstasy'; or Australian 'bush pioneer' romanticism - back to the land! Neither had much to offer communities, and both contributed to the failure of many. From the start, this movement contained conflict - overt and covert - between

those who advocated more communality and those who resisted this, by invoking the value of the 'rugged' individual.

In 1975, Mandala's founders, though informed by communal ideals, attempted a compromise between the forces of individualism and communalism by setting up a company - Mandala Pty Ltd - which advertised 15 private, one hectare leases, on self-selected sites, spread around its 112 hectare property. They did this also because they needed to attract members in a hurry. They had no money, and the contract to purchase the land didn't allow them time to be selective. Effectively, the only qualification for membership, and the right to a private block, was the willingness to lend $4,000 (£1900) in order to help finance the company to purchase the land. Virtually no preparatory work was done on organisation, or group process.

Most foundation members were couples with young children, whose priorities were the aquisition of a cheap block of land in the country, completion of their owner-built dwellings, and the getting of personal income. Communal idealism was soon buried by these personal agendas. Some attempted to live the myth of the self-sufficient homesteader while drawing government benefits, others found work in the district. After bitter disputes, and the departure of the founders, and many others, Mandala became essentially a land owning company, providing security for its lessee members. The community agenda was limited to minimal facilitation of some individual needs.

Our population turned over rapidly in the seventies and early eighties, as members sold their leases and shares to newcomers, many of whom brought a similar unwillingness or inability to be effective members - even in a community which asked so little. While the lease contained clauses giving the company the right to refuse sales of leases, or to exercise a first option to purchase, we never did so, because most of us were unwilling to disadvantage a seller by refusing, or delaying, a sale in what was

One of the private dwellingss at Mandala. Photograph by John Hetherington

never a buoyant market. Also, the company never had the money, or the will to borrow, in order to buy out a lease, and take the time to find a person considered suitable. We could not agree on any criteria for membership anyway.

All communities experience the conflict between 'the centrifugal forces of (the wider) society where personal choice and whim is celebrated, and the centripetal forces needed to keep a social group together'.[1] Mandala, by placing the personal ahead of the communal, was prey to overwhelming centrifugal forces; the flight into 'rural surburbia'. However, I believe Mandala is lucky, in that this flight took place early in its history, with no more than token resistance from a rump of communal diehards - which included this writer. In those early years, we patched together a structure which, with hindsight, served the community well in its pioneering years. It ensured Mandala's physical survival, and gave members the confidence to build comfortable houses, and time to forge links, through work and social contacts, with the wider locality. A core of surviving foundation members, some of whom came to Mandala with very little money, achieved financial security, and raised their children within a community which made few demands on their time and resources.

This minimalist structure, and even our failure to recruit and engender a more cohesive membership, gave us some advantages when we began our movement towards intentional community in 1990. We had the priceless asset of a virtually clean slate, with little baggage, idealogical or organisational, to dump. Within our low-intensity social environment, we had become more experienced and patient, more tolerant of others in our diversity, and less prone to feelings of fear or insecurity. Also, our membership turnover had slowed. We were ageing people, with reduced family responsibilities, and more time to devote (if we so chose) to the community. (Half of Mandala's adult residents are now over 50, two are below 40 and there remain just three school-age children). All actively involved members - some 16 out of 25 adults - carried, in various ways, a torch for intentional community, and shared an awareness of the problem of Mandala's impending generational change. The question of how we might tackle this problem, and our perception that time was short, became a strong additional motivation for us to try to go 'intentional'. The fact that some of us were emerging from the narcissistic broodings of 'the mid-life crisis' into more adventurous communal idealists, with little of value to lose, was an important energiser.

What kind of Intentional Community?
In 1991, a survey of currently active members found two kinds of ambitions for Mandala. Some sought a community which would foster good interpersonal and group relationships, providing emotional, social, and maybe financial support to its members. Others wanted us to work on projects which served shared aims, be a positive influence in the wider society, and make an income in doing so. Following lots of debate, we settled for both, as complementary and essential to each other. It was

not necessary that we debate the virtues of non-coercive, egalitarian, decision making and management - however, we'll argue the details for the rest of our lives! Our best possible egalitarian practice, will ensure that our 'intentions' will be constantly evolving, and will not pave a road to our own little hell.

Our decision to start a community and environmental education centre was the initial focus of Mandala's new intentionality. Remember, this aim was not shared by all shareholders. We needed a new organisational structure, which was appropriate to this next stage of our development, while protecting the individual 'rights' of all - including the minority who were not interested in, or doubtful of, such ventures. In order to pay for guest facilities, and programme development, as well as provide this structure, 15 of us set up and financed a new company - Mandala Community Pty Ltd. At the same time we tidied up, and strengthened, the structure of the original company. Our community is now organised into two companies. All of us, at present, are shareholders in Mandala Pty Ltd, which continues to own the land and look after the personal interests of its leaseholders. Most of us are also shareholders in Mandala Community Pty Ltd, which promotes and serves intentional community, through various commercial and semi-commercial activies. The new company is not a device to produce schism. It is a tool for community growth, which recognises, and allows for, the reality (which applies in all non-coercive communities) of widely-differing levels of commitment.

The new company, in its constitution and organisation, is very different from the original company: *It is selective, granting full membership to individuals only after a period of Associate Membership, and a six-month 'courtship'. Full membership is available to individuals who don't own a share in the original company.*

This gives us the chance to recruit badly-needed young minds and energies, by allowing young adults, including our grown children, to become fully involved, without the need to find the money to buy a share/leaseholding in the land-owning company, or wait for the death of their parents. In the present climate of high youth unemployment and disillusionment, I perceive that many young people in the nineties (unlike the eighties) are looking for social alternatives. They hold a more realistic view of the the world - having had things so much tougher than did their 'baby-boomer' parents in the late sixties. I believe that many of them see possibilities in intentional community which are related to their own insights into the wider social reality, and their own needs.

The new company also gives us the possibility of breaking, gradually, the nexus between property 'ownership' and community membership. The housing on Mandala has become quite elaborate over the years, and while the 'market' hasn't recently been tested, my guess is that many shareholders would be looking for around $100,000 (£48,000) if they sold. Lending institutions don't provide mortgages for multiple-occupancy leases like ours, so buyers are likely to be middle-aged, (and middle-class) people. Our 'success rate' with such people in the past hasn't been too flash. Also, this age group is, as I have shown, hugely over-represented in our membership.

By contrast, the price of Associate Membership is low, associates have the rights of full members, other than a vote on the management committee, and there will be no financial or logistical difficulties if they chose to move on. A turnover of associates will continually refresh and advantage, rather than disadvantage, our community and those who choose to become full members, will have had the best possible apprenticeship.

Housing the next generation of Members
Mandala has a large, under-utilised stock of housing, with several middle-aged couples occupying three-bedroomed houses, each set in a hectare of high maintenance landscaping and gardens. If the

community fails to prepare itself for the realities of human decline and mortality within 20 years these elaborate domestic establishments will be millstones round the necks of elderly, often frail, people - some of them widows or widowers.

As well as providing income for members, the new company includes in its aims the making of profits. If we achieve this, we will be able to provide the resources to house new members in a

---

Chris Coates reviews: *From Utopian Dreaming to Communal Reality* by Bill Metcalf (University of New South Wales Press, 1995) ISBN 0 86840 087 4, available in the UK from Edge of Time - see page 224

"Is the quest for intentional community worthwhile?" Asks Bill Meltcalf in the last chapter of this book about communities in Australia - the previous twelve chapters have already provided the answer a resounding - Yes!

Whilst in no way avoiding the pitfalls and problems of communal life the ten contributors to the book, all from different communities, provide a positive guide to the last twenty years of communal life down-under. And with the Author's chapter on the history of Australian communities going back to the late 1800s this is probably the best book on communities in any particular country I have read.

The contributors are drawn from a wide range of communities, both secular and spiritual, rural and urban. All have notched up many years of "communal reality" and reading their experiences you get the real flavour of communal life from the idealism of the early days of a new community to the - wise after the event - thoughts of old communards. I was struck all through the book, again and again, by the similarities in experiences between the Australian communities and British communities of the same period and even with what I have read of American and European groups. Though I suppose I shouldn't really be surprised. Communal History long ago taught me that people trying to live together face the same problems, wherever or whenever they are, and yes we do have to keep reinventing the wheel.

Whether you are interested in the history of alternative Australia, the thoughts of experienced communards or the daily nitty gritty of communal living this book has something for you. And whilst I would disagree with some of Bill Metcalf's conclusions in the final chapter (which at times seem to be a bit forced and on occasions contradicted by what contributors have said in the previous chapters) on the whole the book is inspirational and gives you the impression that Australians wouldn't give a XXXX for any other way of life.

form of co-housing by either buying the shares and leases of departing members, or non-compulsory transfer from elderly members who wish to stay. This housing will then be available for associate and new, full members.

In this way we may change, gradually, not only the generational 'mix', but the very nature of the community. New full members will be engendered via Associate Membership. The wish to be part of an intentional community, rather than the size of a person's bank balance, will be the main qualification for membership. The individualistic need to protect, or realise maximum financial benefit from, personal 'property rights', will recede as a force in the community.

At the same time, the interests of some of my generation, ten or twenty years from now, may be better served. For example, my partner and I are among those middle-aged couples rattling around in a house which is too big for us. It is a high quality, timber frame building, which may easily be modified. Given that both of us wish to live out our days at Mandala, it may suit us to either sell, or arrange to bequeath, our house to the community. Mandala Community Pty Ltd, as the new owner, or prospective owner, would not need to pay, up front, its full value. Part of the deal could be rent-free occupation of half the (converted) building for the rest of our lives plus a modest 'retirement' income. The other half would be available for younger new members, whose rental arrangement might include taking care of the place, and assisting my partner and I through our dotage.

All this is contingent, of course, on the quality and the pace of our transformation towards intentionality, including the level of our commercial success. Time is short. My generation has, at most, ten years to achieve an intentional community which is a beacon and magnet to the young, rather than a dying refuge for the 'me ... now' generation. We have set up a structure but we need to work on our shared resolve - now fragile and incomplete - and there's lots to do.

I find the alternative to urgent change almost too horrible to contemplate. I envisage aged survivors being 'picked off' one by one by forced sales, in an environment where declining community energy and resources cannot ensure community-minded buyers. Geographically remote, middle-aged heirs, with little interest in the community will be anxious to realise the value of unwanted houses. Possibly, the heirs of only the wealthier among the membership will acquire cheaply an increasingly prime piece of real estate, with an elaborate infrastructure built by voluntary labour. (Wealth inequality at Mandala is an issue not quite yet on our agenda, but the related question of unequal labour inputs is a current hot one). The community will be reduced to a sentimental footnote in a history written by and for its subsumers. Such a fate beckons scores of rural communities in Australia. Some, no doubt, will be pleased to call it 'developmental communalism'.

I do not share the view expressed by my friend Bill Metcalf, that survival, for twenty years or so, is a good measure of a community's 'success'.[2] A pertinent assessment will only be possible when my generation are all dead. I think that success, or otherwise, will then not be measured merely in survival, but in how the future Mandala is thinking, working, being and developing - perhaps in ways you or I now can't even imagine. In the face of the forces of 'rugged' individualism - and the thieving, proprietorial imperative - the odds may be against the making of a truly egalitarian community. But I mean to have fun helping make it possible.

Bill Smale migrated from the UK to Australia in 1964. An anarchist, he has been involved in cooperative living since 1972. In 1975, he was a foundation member of Mandala Community, his home ever since. He contributed a chapter to 'From Utopian Dreaming to Communal Reality'.

1 & 2 **METCALF Dr W (ed)** (1995) *From Utopian Dreaming to Communal Reality* University Of New South Wales Press (Australia).

Permaculture and Communities

JANE HERA

Permaculture is about creating a Permanent Culture - are

permacultural ideas synonymous with concepts of community?

When David Holmgren and Bill Mollison, two pioneering Australians, coined the term Permaculture their definition was reflecting a need for Permanent Agriculture, as they recognised that our current agricultural practises are planet threatening. As Permaculture has grown and spread throughout the world the definition has been enlarged to Permanent Culture in recognition of the fact that all aspects of the way we live require designing from the baseline of sustainability.

Permaculture is the conscious design of the strategies we employ to meet our needs using natural systems as our models. It is an empowering system which encourages us towards self reliance. The starting point is a triangle of ethics.

Beginning with a clear statement of ethics may seem to be stating the obvious for some of us but is well worth doing. Especially if we consider how our current culture would appear if its unstated ethics of maximum

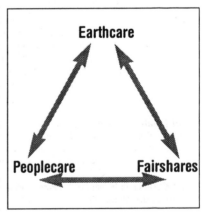

profit for the few, with no consideration for people or the planet, were more openly acknowledged.

Earthcare means the provision for all life systems to continue and multiply.

Peoplecare means the provision for all people to access those resources necessary to their existence. This includes emotional and spiritual as well as material resources.

Fairshares means the distribution of resources to these ends. It includes a commitment to setting limits to population and consumption. This commitment is particularly relevant in the rich countries of the world, where the birth of every child means the use of many more resources than it does in the two thirds world.

The reason that members of communities are in a good position to take Permaculture on board is that they have already taken a conscious decision to step away from the traditional models of living, they have already "broken out" at some level. This can be a useful starting point for engaging in Permaculture.

I am not going to describe the design details of herb spirals, mulched vegetable beds, forest gardens, rainwater collection systems, compost toilets, reed beds, aquacultures, self forage poultry systems etc as these are brilliantly described elsewhere by others (see book recommendations). Suffice it to say that the application of Permaculture principles provides creative solutions, enabling us to interconnect many hitherto unrelated elements to more easily meet our needs.

As well as clearly defining an ethical base from which to begin Permaculture also provides a common language with which to work. This can greatly assist those communities which spend much of their valuable time making decisions in large groups in order to adhere to democratic principles. There is a very useful model called the three group model which suggests that any group bigger than three is too large to make decisions and that, after feeding in their opinions on any matter a large group should delegate a group of three to go off and make the decision. It becomes easier to trust others to make the right decisions for us when we share with them a common language like Permaculture with the ethics and principles that that entails.

Another useful Permaculture position is colloquially called "no whynchas". Whynchas are people who say " Why don't you do this and why don't you do that" without offering to provide the full resource to make it happen themselves and effectively proposing work that others should do. We probably have a British equivalent (this model comes from Australia) of "We oughtas", those people who continually say we ought to do this or that because they believe it is what is supposed to happen, but without making reference to whether it's what we actually want or are able to do. We have a saying in the Permaculture community which is "Put up (put up the resources, energy and enthusiasm to help or redirect) or shut up (don't complain about how other people are doing it) ".

Communities can often feel overwhelmed by the number of tasks that need doing and Permaculture principles help to make priorities clear. For example "Begin at your own back door", "start small and work out from well managed areas" and "repair first" are very helpful guidelines. Likewise the concept of zoning in Permaculture helps us minimise energy inputs to a site, especially our own, by thoughtful arrangement of elements in the system so that herbs and vegetables need to be within sight of the kitchen window and easy distance from the back door, chickens or other livestock that require frequent visiting need to be close to our centre of activity and fruit trees and grain crops, which require less frequent visits can be further away.

Careful and protracted observation is a key element in beginning, developing and managing a Permaculture design. There may be feelings of wanting to get on and do it as quickly as possible, but observing a site for a year so that it is seen in all seasons can provide valuable design information. The detailed mapping of the site, to include existing vegetation and microclimates, can usefully be done during the observation period. Repair work can also be undertaken during this time. For example, areas suffering from erosion can be planted up to minimise further damage.

Many communities are undertaking big projects with the minimum of resources and Permaculture thinking can contribute to them having realistic expectations. Although the money it costs to hire in a consultant may seem like an extravagant expense calling in an experienced designer sooner rather than later will have enormous benefits. The names and addresses of Permaculture Designers are available via The Designers Register from the Permaculture Association (address at end of article).

Some Guiding Principles of Permaculture Design

1 Beneficial, functional relationships (relative location)
2 Multiple functions for single elements
3 Multiple elements for single functions (for security)
4 Energy use and (re-)cycling
5 Use of biological systems
6 Energy efficient planning (zones, sectors and elevation)
7 Appropriate technology
8 Natural succession/stacking
9 Diversity

Otherwise there are many Permaculture Design courses on offer in Britain and Community members can train up to do their own designing.

I am currently part of a project (The Oxfordshire CoHousing Group) which is at the beginning stages of designing an intentional community. There are several of us in the group who are trained permaculture designers and having this expertise on board enables me to be confident about the decisions that fellow group members are taking on my behalf. Knowing that we are working from a common ethical base creates a sense of shared vision and a security about us being able to trust each other.

Since I took a Permaculture Design Course in 1992 I have noticed that any sense of desperation I have about the state of the world has greatly diminished. Learning Permaculture theory and practise has enabled me to start growing some of my own food in a very small urban garden. I have become more empowered in the way I act in the world instead of being angry at "them". Knowing that there are solutions to all of the difficulties we are facing has given me great confidence. This has meant that I have started several community based projects, including a Local Exchange Trading System (LETSystem), a Permaculture Trading System (Permaculture Exchange) and the CoHousing Group.

Being involved with these projects I have come across people who have a lot of desperation about "doing something *now*". Having Permaculture thinking on board, which emphasises protracted and thoughtful observation, has been most helpful. It is clear to me that projects which are begun in a hurry without enough basic design at the outset stand much less of a chance of enduring than those which have moved more slowly at the outset.

Permaculture came about partly as a response to the frustrations of protest, in which people use a lot of energy to say what they don't want. My thinking now is that it is more useful and empowering to say what we do want and to go about working on how to make these visions real in the world. The whole of human culture is undergoing change and transition. I feel myself to be part of a team that has chosen to design these changes. I am engaged in a process of conscious evolution out of the classist, sexist, racist mess that capitalism supports and towards a sustainable culture.

I can already tell, from the increased independence that has come from growing some of my own food and from going for lifestyle changes chosen for sustainability over the last few years that I'm in a much stronger position to make sure that my own good thinking and that of others comes alive and happens on the ground.

Jane Hera is a Permaculture Designer working with Designed Visions, 8 Helen Road Oxford OX2 0DE. She took her first Permaculture Design course in May 1991 and since then has taught and facilitated on many other Permaculture Courses. She obtained the Diploma in Permaculture Design in September 1994. Jane lives in Oxford with her partner Andy and daughter Roben. They run their Practice from a small office in their terraced house where they continue to develop a highly productive urban edible landscape and a low consumption lifestyle.

Recommended reading
- **Bill Mollison** *Permaculture - A Designers' Manual*
- **Bill Mollison** *An Introduction to Permaculture*
- **Patrick Whitefield** *Permaculture in a Nutshell*

The above books and many more are available from Eco-logic books, 19 Maple Grove, Bath BA2 3AF.
- **Permaculture Magazine**
  Hyden House, Little Hyden Lane, Clanfield, Hampshire PO8 0RU.
- **Permaculture Association** P O Box 1, Buckfastleigh, Devon TQ11 0LH.
- **Oxfordshire CoHousing Group** care of 8 Helen Road, Oxford OX2 0DE

LETS and Communes

PETE NORTH

At first sight LETS schemes seem to move practices of bartering and skill sharing, common in intentional communities, out to the community economy. But, apart from making links with the wider world, are LETS of any use to communes? The jury is still out.

Many readers of *Diggers and Dreamers* will have come across Local Exchange Trading Systems, or LETS. Since the first system was established in 1987 approximately 400 systems have mushroomed around the UK, with about 15,000 participants according to LETSLink UK. LETS essentially is an extension of bartering, or an attempt to create a non-money (or local currency) economy parallel to the conventional (sterling) economy. Through membership of LETS people involved in the system trade with each other using a form of local currency or 'Green Dollar' (in Manchester they are called 'Bobbins', 'Olivers' in Bath, 'Favours' in Bristol, 'Wharfes' in Ilkley - and 'Brads' in Bradford). LETS systems grow organically from small origins to larger systems such as that in Manchester (400 members), West Wiltshire or Stroud.

LETS advocates see LETSystems as a tool, and no more. They argue that LETS by itself need not be seen as a radical challenge to mainstream society, and that LETS, like the mutual aid societies of the 19th Century (the Co-op, friendly societies, building societies) has the potential to become an accepted part of mainstream life. If joining a Building Society was once a fairly subversive thing to do, now having a mortgage makes you part of the property owning democracy. The question for LETS is whether this tool, using local currencies, is a step on the road to a more sustainable and communal world, or whether LETS will become part of the mainstream but in no sense a challenge to the status quo. Key to this will be to examine the potential for LETS reaching those the mainstream economy doesn't, and making their lives more livable.

LETS by and large has not yet taken off in the communities that could most benefit from it - on outer housing estates, the inner city, and among unemployed people and those excluded from the money economy. The major barriers to LETS really benefiting such communities are overcoming the inbuilt fear of "debt" with the idea of "commitment", and overcoming the worry that LETS will affect benefit. Perhaps LETS will not really take off until it is part of the mainstream economy; when businesses are members of LETS so the basic staples of life are available for local currency (at present the most you can hope for is in-season organic vegetables). Or when rent can be paid in local currency, a system a co-op in Hulme is hoping to develop. Or when the local council takes rent and local taxes in local currency, or income tax is payable locally and spent locally. To put it starkly, this all seems a long way off.

For this author LETS should not attempt to become part of the mainstream. LETS should locate itself clearly alongside communes, with what has recently been called 'DIY culture' or what Dauncey (1987) calls the rainbow economy, not with trying to become a 21st Century equivalent of the Halifax Building Society. The potential for LETS revitalising countercultural ideas is massive; LETS can be truly liberating, giving access to a flexible lifestyle where members work a few hours a day and do a number of jobs for their community. It is step towards a communal society of "from each according to their ability, to each according to their needs" or a society where as Marx put it one can "hunt in the morning, fish in the afternoon, rear cattle in the evening and be a literary critic after dinner, without ever becoming a hunter, a fisherman, a herdsman, or a critic". Like the Communes movement, LETS fits with a bottom-up, decentralist vision of social change, with the socialism of William Morris rather than that of Lenin.

joining a Building Society was once a fairly subversive thing to do

LETSystems, like communes, should be seen as prefigurative organisations for a future green society: but unlike communes, they have the potential to reach far more people for the simple reason that cost of access to LETS is very low. Participation in LETS does not require the same level of all out commitment as joining a commune, or even of joining a worker co-op. If communes require members to embark on a new life by living together communally, perhaps withdrawing from the mainstream economy and living as self sufficiently as possible, LETS requires a much lower level of commitment. But paradoxically, this low level of commitment may be its downfall, and may compromise LETSystems ability to contribute to social change without help from, amongst others, the communes movement. In isolation it is doubtful whether LETS is more than what Coleman called "a group effort to 'shop for a better world'"(1994). He warns us not to mistake co-operative organising for little more than odd jobbing, access to a new social network of like minded people, rather than a prefigurative new world. Lang (1994) reports that LETS members often see the system giving access to a new and more full social life (which is to be welcomed, and helps build feelings of community) but perhaps LETS members also need exposure to the example of deeper communal experiences through communes.

The radical concern is that LETS, rather than building a co-operative society, does little more than monetise pre-existing human relations. The sharing and co-operation that friends and neighbours do anyway without the need for LETS - the "I owe you one" is replaced by an onerous recording of commitment. For Offe and Heinz (1987) LETS could lead to the "death of altruism".

Unless it is seen as part of a radical transformation of society, LETS may be creating new entrepreneurs rather than a communitarian society based on mutual aid. As Pepper asked of communes, the question for the LETS community is whether LETS changes society or is being changed by it (Pepper 1990). In isolation LETS is quite Thatcherite, an example of the way that the ideology of the enterprise culture is affecting Greens. LETS by itself does not challenge the status quo or redistribute wealth, and too often it recreates the inequalities of the conventional economy within the system (Wall 1990).

To remedy these doubts the LETS community needs to learn from communards' experience. As a contribution to building a Green society, it is doubtful that LETS has enough of what Kantor (1972) called "commitment building mechanisms", the day to day contacts and mechanisms that get people to break down their individualism and to think, feel and act as a community. Like the co-op, and unlike communes, there perhaps is not enough co-operative living embodied in LETS. Simply having an alternative place to buy organic vegetables or get a massage you otherwise would not have been able to afford, or even having your life significantly enhanced by getting things done on LETS, may still not be enough if the objective is a more communal society. Isolated trading may be inadequate as no feelings of community are engendered, or as George William Russell put it, "No true social organism has been created. If people unite as consumers to buy together they only come in contact on this one point; there is no general identity of interest".

LETS and communes can benefit each other tremendously. LETSystems can provide a way of making community businesses, including those run by communes, more viable by aiding cash flow, providing a ready supply of customers and method of marketing, and more risk free innovation. LETS makes such businesses real contributors to the development of an alternative, people centred economy in which alternatives to competition with capitalist businesses on their terms is possible (see Landry et al, 1985), and a business that may not be viable in sterling may well be in local currency. As those commissioning work now have access to a relatively unlimited supply of currency the opportunity exists for occupations that have a low status in the conventional economy, like childminding or repairwork, but which people would use if they could afford it, to become more highly valued.

In contrast to those critics who chastise LETS for its high concentration of tarot card readers and alternative health practitioners, in a community economy setting the contribution of LETS in revaluing economic activity in a communitarian way is fully recognised. These services, not valued conventionally but which are at best a real contribution to a rich lifestyle and at least make life more livable and fun, become accessible to those without money to spare. Alternative health practitioners and educationalists find a new market - and commune members can provide these services making a commune that would not be viable in the conventional economy more likely to succeed.

LETS would provide a method of linking the commune to potential supporters and members, and a wider community network in which the ideals of a commune can be spread (breaking the isolation some communes feel but maintaining enough of a border with the outside world). The commune would, effectively, be supported by the wider community and provide a next step for people who want to move further away from the conventional economy into a community economy. Communes can strengthen the commitment and community building elements of LETS and provide a welcome source of attraction back to LETS' Green origins which are in danger of being forgotten. Communes can provide a welcome push away from accommodation with mainstream society that is experienced by LETS systems.

If it is going to benefit those who really need it, and contribute to social progress, the LETS movement needs to think more clearly about where it stands politically, and to move away from its current craving for respectability. LETSystems need to contribute towards the development of a wider movement towards the community economy along with Communes, Co-ops, Community Land Banks, Community Businesses, Future Imagining workshops, Planning for Real exercises. LETS can provide a scaffold linking these initiatives together, creating a social economy network, parallel to the capitalist economy, but one that cannot be easily criticised as little more than an island in a capitalist sea. LETS can be a ladder into the social economy and the social economy a ladder into the Green society.

A radical conception of LETS sees in the building of the Social Economy a radical transformation of society; as theorised by Martin Buber in his 1947 book "Paths in Utopia". Buber specifically rejects Marx's dictum that the task of this generation is only to struggle against capitalism and to avoid thinking and experimenting about what socialism might be like. Socialism, for Buber, is not struggle 'against' but 'for' what he calls "the structured renewal of the cell tissue of society". Progress for Buber is fighting for the maximum degree of communal autonomy possible so that a full human life is livable in a future socialist society. Without such work in the present, he argued, human beings will not be ready for a more free world.

"There can be pseudo realisation of socialism, where the real life of man to man is but little changed. The real living together of man with man can only thrive where people have the real things of their common life in common; where they can experience, discuss and administer them together; where real fellowships and real work guilds exist." (Buber 1947 p41)

In Buber's conception, the task for LETS supporters is to join with communards in the building of
a federation of trade and communal associations cris-
crossing each other and interconnecting. These
will form:

> *"the germ of the new social form which will sup-*
> *plant the old ... This society will be composed of a*
> *number of societies banded together for everything*
> *that demands a common effort: federations of produc-*
> *ers for all kinds of production, of Societies for con-*
> *sumption ... more extensive groups embracing a whole*
> *country or even several countries and composed of*
> *persons who will work in common for the satisfaction*
> *of ... economic, spiritual and artistic needs. (Buber*
> *1947, p42)*

Communards have perhaps always known this:
they need to communicate their experiences to
the LETS community, and LETSystems can bring
an important gift to communes. Before LETS, a
conception that countercultural initiatives could lead
to wider social change was perhaps always unre-
alistic, and while a full and happy life is lived by
many communards, communes as a wider catalyst
for social change were perhaps always doomed to
eventual isolation and containment. The advent of
this new tool for social change, the LETSystem, potentially changes the environment in which communal lifestyles can be developed by facilitating more
extensive linkages between communes and the
wider world in which they swim. And Communards
need to become closely involved in the LETS community if LETSystems are to avoid the fate of
building societies or the co-op, and to be a radical
tool rather than a part of the mainstream.

Pete North of Bristol University has never lived in a commune which he regards
as one of his life's great disappointments. Following a few years attempting to
inflict economic development on some of Britain's cities, he is writing his PhD on
the politics of LETS. Concentrating on the experience of one of the UK's largest
LETSystems in Manchester, he sees in LETS a revival of the bottom-up traditions
of eco-socialism of William Morris and Robert Owen.

Communes and Lovestyles

KIAN DE LA COUR

Burn your karma in the flames of spiritual polyfidelity!

In August 1994 I attended PEPCON's 8th annual conference at Harbin Hot Springs, California. PEP stands for Polyfidelitous Educational Productions and their conference was subtitled "Loving More: Transforming Relationships"(I translate polyfidelity as meaning faithful to more than one. Some people have a looser definition). Transforming from monogamy and an often toxic family environment to polyfidelity, which they propose offers "more love, more growth, more intimacy, more commitment". Ryam Nearing of PEP has written: "Monogamy may be a valid choice for some people at some times, but we also need other legitimate options for intimacy and family life. Our goal is new kinds of relationships based on unconditional love, continuing spiritual growth, respect for our diversity, equality among partners, telling the truth about our deepest desires, and accepting personal responsibility ... together we explore the total transformation of love, sex, and the family!"

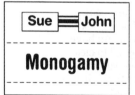

I had been exploring responsible non-monogamy for a while and wanted to meet others living this in their communities. The term "non-monogamy" is prefaced here by "responsible" to distance it from swinging, which there was a noticable lack of at the conference. These people were serious! Most people attending had had much experience of living in an extended family of some kind it seemed; there were a number of people from well known group living projects such as Kerista (now defunct) and ZEGG (of which more

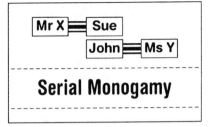

later). We attended workshops on cross-cultural and sociobiological precedents for poly-living; gender balancing; how to build a polyfedelitous family; queers in family; relationships as a vehicle for personal/spiritual growth; techniques to facilitate a transparency of communication (the need for honesty); financial options in group marriage; tribal tantra; "coming out" as poly, and much, much more. It was enlightening.

Poly Philosophy

The basic premise seems to be that it is natural to be attracted to a number of people and that to bring this to its logical conclusion of being sexually intimate with more than one person, and have them all get on as a family, has the potential to clear many blocks in the individual's paths to growth (many things are likely to have to be dealt with for it to work) and also to build intimate, caring and therefore strong communities. Strong communities are also developed by those who share an interest in this way of living as we come together in groups to share our experience and practice the technologies for growth often deemed necessary to this kind of relationship. Dr. Deborah Anapol states in "Love Without Limits: The Quest for Sustainable Intimate Relationships" that she sees some kind of energy practice such as Tantra necessary because they increase overall health, stamina and hap-

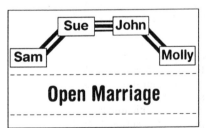

piness and because they can teach you to open up and consciously channel sexual energy which will be useful in dealing with feelings and in becoming fully present in any situation. Honesty and consciousness are very much prized by all I have met interested in multi-partner relationships.

Ryam Nearing's polyfidelity primer "Loving More" states that studies are steadily shattering the myth of monogamy. "The number of mamal species now believed to be monogamous is now down to 2%". Birds do it, elk do it ... Monogamy is going the way of the nuclear family in that it is held to be the norm, but in fact is the exception. Strictly speaking monogamy means one sex partner for life. This is manifestly uncommon. What most people do is serial monogamy - or what Deborah Anapol calls serial non-monogamy (lots of partners seperated by linear time). While many people profess to monogamy, a very large number have intimate and/or sexual relations outside of their primary relationships - and then lie about it! One of Deborah's most powerful quotes is "We have as a people grown afraid to love when the spirit moves us." The overwhelming characteristic of monogamy is limitation/repression of self and partner. Dr Wilhelm Reich's "The Mass Psychology of Fascism" clearly deliniates the relationship between sexual repression and authoritarian conditioning (itself the subtitle of a recent book "The Irrational in Politics" by Maurice Brinton).

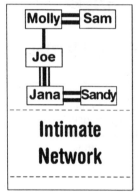

Intimate Network

Whereas modern "love" often proves to be an addiction, and one which bolsters the economy to boot, responsible non-monogamy demands that we recognise our profound connection to other people and truly honour it. To be able to do so we must heal ourselves. Shared loving accelerates this healing and close bonding of individuals and if we are to contribute to the planet's clean-up, this can only be an advantage (for more on this line of thought see Dolores LaChapelle's "Sacred Land, Sacred Sex, Rapture of the Deep: Concerning Deep Ecology and Celebrating Life").

Communal sexuality
Many people interested in multi-partner relationships choose to live together and have pioneered experiments in shared property and wealth to the great advantage of others - monogamous or otherwise - choosing to live together. The variety of arrangements is limited only by the imagination. At PEPCON I learned of a journal devoted exclusively to sharing the results of experimental finance/property arrangements so that experience is pooled and mistakes don't have to be repeated! Where communal living differs from whatever the alternative is called is in its demotion of personal possession. Responsible non-monogamy is in continuum with this aim. While direct experience must be regarded as having the greatest content, not all communes may wish to explore this avenue. Nevertheless there remain valuable lessons to be learnt from the experience of others. There is a resource list included for those interested in taking this any further.

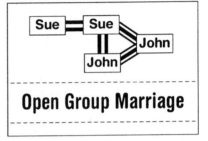

Open Group Marriage

There is a wealth of data here which is not easy to come by so I will limit myself to providing a brief run down of a few of the larger polyfidelitous communities.

The nineteenth century Oneida community (1848-1881) in America is an example of a commune devoted to the practice of non-possessive love styles. Believing marriage to be oppresive and sex liberating, exclusive pair bonding was here forbidden in favour of sexual freedom. Children lived in a Children's House and exclusive attatchments to their biological parents was strongly discouraged.

Housework and other work was collectivized and performed equally by both genders. Whilst researching for this article I encountered an astonishing reference to Oneida and energy work/tantra in Louis T Culling's classic "Sex Magick" as follows: "[T]he Oneida Community ... practiced the interchange of husbands and wives as a magickal practice, to give a greater unity and spiritual strength to the entire community group. This was excellent magick. The climax was forbidden in these "agape unions" to avoid offspring complications. Because this congrex was held under both the rules of communal love and religious aspiration, there was no resultant frustration because of the absence of climax." By the time Oneida closed due to outside pressure they had two hundred and eighty-eight members and ran a highly successful business.

That sex and other intimate behaviour is a powerful bonding mechanism is recognised by the profusion of centers dedicated to training people in the tradition of Rajneesh/Osho. Here the aim is to create a theraputic and loving environment so that rejection and jealousy are easily handled or cease to become an issue. This is because; first, one is loved by such a number of people, and so deeply, that the temporary "loss" of a lover is no great hardship and; second, because one is given the space and emotional freedom to fully express and work through any considerations that do come up.

The above is a vision of an erotic community dedicated to self expression. This model is also used by the "Actions-Analytical Organization for conscious life praxis" or AAO (1970 - ? [at least 1982]) except that they dispense with the hierarchical mode of organization which was employed at Oneida and is still employed to some extent at many Osho communes even though their guru is dead. In 1977 the AAO defined themselves thus: "an important social experiment with common property, free sexuality, common economy, direct democracy, collective children and spontaneous emotional self expression. The AAO is not a utopian vision of an ideal society, it is an existing model for a new social life praxis. the AAO is the practical proof that it is possible to live together without aggression and the use of violence, without sexual repression. the AAO has been in existance for eight years and at the present 500 people live in the twelve AA groups in Western Europe and the States."

Of course, even the AAO are not free of value judgements. They were (in 1977) self consciously identified with Reich and took on board much of his Marxist ideology. They also exhibited a degree of apparent intolerance in the form of homophobia.

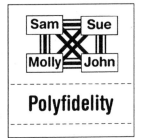

At this time, the pioneering spirit of the above ventures is being vigorously expressed in Germany and elsewhere in the shape of ZEGG (Centre for Experimental Cultural Design). ZEGG is a commune of 88 adults and twelve children that has been developing for the past 15 years. "We need to find the main causes of fear and violence between people, understand them, and develop a way of living together on a new basis. At ZEGG, living together itself is a process of research and development, where new social structures are put to the test. Anything can be tried that might make life more interesting, more lively, more sensual.

"There cannot be peace between nations as long as there is war between the sexes. We are not free, and no society is free as long as love and sexuality are surrounded by so much pretense, phoniness, silence, and lies. No one is free as long as our greatest longing is permanently linked to our greatest fear. A person is free when he or she is able to love and allowed to love freely. In fact. there can be no such thing as 'unfree' love. Love is always free and everything else is a misunderstanding."

An American project which has developed out of ZEGG is called Balthiel, "named after the angel Balthiel from the Testament of Solomon; the only angel of the seven planetary angels to overcome the entanglements of the evil genius of jealousy"

As well as focussing on issues of personal growth, transparent communication, open sexuality and innovative community building, they research areas of energy physics; healing; resonance technology; they have designed their own non-polluting heating system; water treatment facility using marsh plants and no chemicals; a non-chemical self-powered antannae swimming pool cleaning system. They keep an organic garden and have a dolphin research ship which explores human-whale-dolphin communication off the west coast of Africa. Thus ZEGG is not a "single issue" concern in the way some places of sexual healing/experimentation are; unless that single issue be wholism.

ZEGG provides an excellent model of free sexuality working harmoniously in a community, itself developing and at the same time providing energy and incentive for development of other related areas of human experience. In this way free sexuality can be a powerful source of individual and group empowerment. I recommend you follow up some of the resources below listed on page 56!

"People doing it say 'There is something magical about this lifestyle to me ... because it is living an alternative, it's living a contradiction to all the standard programming and the way that everyone expects you to be. Whenever you are doing something that is different from the norm, there is a magic to it, a freedom and a sense of power. I always have a feeling that if we can do this thing that is so delicate and complicated, even for a few years, we can do anything'." from "Loving More: The Polyfidelity Primer".

Kian de la Cour is a sacred intimate, gonzo journalist, ecstatic, drummer musician, Avatar, erotic explorer and masseur. E (sic) was raised in and around communes and has visited many in the UK, USA and Denmark. Other interests include myth and ritual, genderwork and seizing thee (sic) media. Contact him c/o Sex Zine (see page 56) or electronic mail: headmail@phreak.intermedia.co.uk

ORGANISATIONS PROMOTING
SACRED/COMMUNAL SEXUALITY.

AAO Berlin *Bulowstr 90, D-1000 Berlin
30, Germany* ✆ *0049 (0)30 262 33 60.*

AAO Vienna *Praterstr 32/2/12, A-1020
Wien, Austria* ✆ *0043 (0)222 26 51 32.*

AAO Paris *5-7 rue du 14 juillet, F-94700
Maisons-alfort, France* ✆ *0033 2 07 52 81.*

The Art of Being (UK) *17 Edith Road,
Faversham, Kent, ME13 8SD.*
✆ *01795-535867.*

Art Rosenblum, Aquarian Alternatives *5620
Morton Street, Philadelphia, PA
19144-1330, USA* ✆ *001 215 849 1259
or 215 849 3237.*

Body Electric Europe *Waterloostr 3, 22769
Hamburg, Germany.*

Intinet Resource Centre *PO Box 4322, San
Rafael, CA 94913-4322, USA
✆ 001 415 507 1739,
E-mail: pad@well.sf.ca.usa*

Network for a New Culture *PO Box 14183,
Scottsdale, AZ 85267-4183, USA.*

Osho Multiversity London *c/o C Harding,
8 Manor Road, Rusthall, Kent,
TN4 8UE.* ✆ *01892-544998.*

PEP (Polyfidelitous Educational Productions)
*PO Box 6306, Captain Cook, HI 96704,
USA.* ✆ *001 808 929 9691 (9-9 Pacific
Standard Time) or Fax 808 929 9831
(anytime). E-mail via modem on The
WELL: 001 415 332 6106 - "pepsyn"*

ZEGG *Rosa Luzemberg Str 39, 14806
Belzig, Germany.* ✆ *0049 (0)33 841
59510, Fax 033 841 59512 (see
Overseas listing, page 215).*

BOOKS: ESSENTIAL READING!

ANAPOL, A *(1992)* **Love Without Limits: The
Quest for Sustainable Intimate Relationships -
Responsible Non-Monogamy** *Intinet
Resource Centre, California. $16 from
IRC above; or £12.95 from The Private
Case, PO Box 23, Royston, Hertford-
shire, SG8 8DT.*

SKOPIK, B *(translator) (1977)* **The AA
Model** *AA verlag, Nurenberg.*

BRINTON, M *(1993)* **The Irrational in Politics:**

Sexual Repression & Authoritarian Conditioning
*Sharp Press, AZ. $6 from PO Box
1731, Tucson, AZ 85702-1731; or
£4.95 (older pressing) from: AK
Distribution, 22 Luton Place,
Edinburgh EH8 9PE.*
✆ *and Fax: 0131 667 1507.*

LaChapelle, D *(1988)* **Sacred Land, Sacred
Sex: Rapture Of The Deep: Concerning Deep
Ecology And Celebrating Life** *Kivaki Press,
CO. $25 from (or enquires to) Kivaki
Press, 585 east 31st Street, Durango,
CO 81301, USA.*

Nearing, R *(1992)* **Loving More: The
Polyfidelity Primer** *PEP Publishing,
Captain Cook. $12. Contact: PEP (see
above).*

*Safer Planet Sex: The Handbook Massive
listing of everything to do with sex, in
Britain & worldwide. Directions, playing, travelling, shopping, performing,
looking, reaching, talking. £8 from
Tuppy Owens, PO Box 4ZB, London,
W1A 4ZB.*

Wolf, L *(1993)* **Women Who May Never Marry:
the reasons, realities and opportunuties**
*Longstreet Press, GA. ISBN: 1 56352
092 3. Contact: Longstreet Press, c/o
Cox Newspapers, 2140 Newmarket
Parkway, Suite 118, Marietta, GA
30067, USA.*

ZINES & NEWSLETTERS

Intinet Resource Centre Newsletter

PEP Newsletter

*Both organisations publish excellent
newsletter. Contact them for details.*

Compersion *A newsletter from ZEGG.*

Sex Zine *"for a liberatory sexuality"
covers non-monogamy and related
areas. Issues 1 & 2, £1.25 each (in
stamps) from: Head Read, BM Uplift,
London, WC1N 3XX. Send 2 x 1st
class stamps for an intro to non-
monogamy.*

EIDOS (Everyone Is Doing Outrageous Sex)
*Large format feminist/libertarian jour-
nal of sexual freedom. $10 from: PO
Box 96, Boston, MA 02137-0096, USA.*

Patrick Upton reviews: *Is it Utopia Yet?* by Kat Kinkade (Twin Oaks Publishing, 1994 ISBN 0 9640445 0 1) available in the UK from Edge of Time Ltd - see page 224)

I'm not sure I'd get on with Kat Kinkade which is a pity, because she's written a really fine book about life inside one of the best known of the secular based, intentional communities in the United States, Twin Oaks. On the face of it Kat and I have a lot in common. We've both spent much of the last two decades in our respective communities, I live at LauriestonHall. Both communities rose out of the radical movements for positive change which flourished in the late 60s and early 70s. Both sought - and still seek - to create a home and workplace where co-operation is the norm, where individuals and the group prosper in harmony. Both communities are healthy, growing older with an ageing population.

My first response to the book was excitement. At last a community "old hand" has written the inside story: no journalist or sociologist with hidden agendas, but a plain ordinary member! The stuff she writes about is totally familiar. Yes, there's an Atlantic Ocean between us, but the chapter headings alone suggested common territory: "Money Equality"; "Collective Consumption"; "The Serenity to Accept the Things I Cannot Change"; "Sex, Love and Jealousy", etc. etc. Having read it, I wanted to sit down and write Laurieston's history to see how we compare.

This is a book to learn from, whether you are already in a community or contemplating joining or helping start one. For example, Laurieston Hall is in the process of discussing whether to go ahead with a grand new-build project. Kat's history of building at Twin Oaks - the intense pressures that puts on some people; the time and energy taken to reach good group decisions; the gap between decision and action resulting once in an unwanted building - all these points made me think more carefully about how "new-build" might be here. She ends by saying: "I no longer think we can build any building without hard feeling somewhere along the line. People who oppose building in general will frequently also oppose it in particular and be critical rather than encouraging of the builders." Hmmmm!*

Kat is always looking for positive ways to improve Twin Oaks, to improve the life of the communards. Her analysis of the problems and successes is there to show how things have ebbed and flowed over the years. But how can any one person - however insightful - give us the story of a community over the last 25 years? Kat does this by mixing personal anecdote with analysis. But I find myself more comfortable with this book when I read it as autobiography. Kat's presence is large on every page and it is this which to quite a large degree gives it verve and sparkle. The trade off for the intensity of insight, the lucidity of Kat's overview is the missing opinions of other members, the ones who skulk in the background, who don't go to meetings. In a way it reminds me of all those school histories of the deeds of kings, queens, & noblemen which ignore the views of the 99% of ordi-

nary folk. There are plenty of names mentioned, though. Some even get potted biographies - from the great and the good to those who steal or try to cheat on the famous labour credit system.

Kat asks the rhetorical question: "How can I stand to live here, where I am obviously a misfit?" Her answer seems basically to be that whilst Twin Oaks isn't everything she would wish, it is better than anything on offer "out there". "Since I seem to have to choose between living with strangers who believe in profit and success and strangers who believe in love and peace, I picked the nicer bunch." Almost sounds sad, that, or is it arrogant? Kat is not fond of 'New Agers'or poor thinkers either. "I tend to avoid philosophical conversation. What I discuss instead are plans and proposals and predicted consequences for our particular Community for various courses of action."

So 'The Microwave Story' she reluctantly prints is quite central to understanding where Kat is coming from. It rings lots of bells for me as an older member of this community. Kat is offered a microwave and accepts it so she can heat food up in the basement where she is learning piano during lunch. She put up a notice saying what she'd done and that any body could use it. "The response was immediate and ferocious. Some people said that there hadn't been any process and that it was improper to make a major change this way ... I kept saying there are no rules against microwaves" Well, yes Kat, but there are probably no rules against gold plated wind vanes. The ensuing uproar led to Kat feeling that she was being got at partly because she was one of the older

members who had exempted themselves from the rules that applied to others. Kat is rather flippant about the ensuing meetings, mocking other people's view point and pointing out the irony that everyone loved her once she gave in and unplugged the machine. "Ultimately I got more pleasure out of the whole mess than out of a whole year's worth of hot lunches".

Kat is pushy. Communities need some pushy people, but it's not good if they become alienated from "the masses". Kat was well aware of the furore bringing the microwave in might create, but she writes "I had found that people quickly got used to new things once somebody dared to introduce them". Yes, that's true, but sometimes the "getting used to" is a harrowing time, even threatening friendships. An apparently trivial piece of hardware can force the community to look seriously at itself, much to it's own astonishment. I wouldn't want this to change. You should hear us discussing the washing machines? And I can remember a wee rumpus here over a strimmer a few years back. This whole story made me aware of a crucial distinction between us and Twin Oaks: we don't have rules, we have guidelines and decisions. (We tried to make rules once and got as far as "No bicycles in the kitchen"). The guidelines and decisions are meant to be observed. Times change, people change. A meeting, or series of meetings updates them and from the very next morning we begin our drift away from them ...

Enough! Get hold of this book. Visit Twin Oaks. Start a new community! Write the history of your Community. Better still, perhaps, write a group history ...

Apocalypse When?

LEE JONES

In the mind of tabloid journalists cults and communes are

inextricably linked. Although it is undoubtedly true that a lot of

people in cults live communally it's equally true that a lot of

people who live communally would be the last people that you'd

find in a cult.

Why an article on cults? Many cults live in some kind of communal group. Some entries in Diggers and Dreamers *might be descibed as cults - at least one was featured in a recent* Observer Magazine *series, "The A to Z of Cults"[1]. As individuals, we the editors have not always approved of the beliefs and practices of some groups who have submitted entries. We have discussed whether or not to include them. But we have always reached the same conclusion: that people should be able to read about all types of groups and judge for themselves who to visit or join. Because our own beliefs are left-liberal-green, we would probably not wish to include any overtly right wing, or racist communal groups. But we've never had such an entry. (In America, where many right wing survivalist communal groups exist, there doesn't appear to be any interest from either side to include them in the New Age/Green communal directories.)*

When we started D&D back in 1989, our intention was to portray the widest possible spectrum of communal groups. In the first edition we used definitions from Abrams and McCulloch[2] to explain that there are four different types of living situation in which communalism is practiced.[3] Most of the Directory entries are types they describe as 'family communes', 'purposive communes' or 'quasi-communes'. In these, communal living is chosen by the individual primarily for what the community has to offer.

In the fourth type, the 'utopian communities', "... the people in them are committed foremost to the transformation of society in accordance with the political or religious beliefs to which the community adheres; and have willingly subordinated personal self interest to those of the community and its goals".[4] Communal living is not their primary reason for joining the group, and yet they "... knowingly and willingly ... share some aspects of living accommodation and material goods".[5]

However, as this article by Lee Jones explores, whilst the term "cult" has achieved the status of notoriety reserved usually for "terrorist" in the popular press, what a cult is exactly and whether they are all such a public menace, remains unclear.

In the spring of 1995 the sinister gassing of Japanese commuters on the Tokyo subway was attributed to the Aum Shinri Kyo sect whose guru, Shoko Asahara, went missing around the time of the first attack on 20th March. On that day twelve people were killed and 5,500 injured. Memories were revived of a series of shocking and tragic events involving cults which spanned the quarter century since the ritual murder of film star Sharon Tate and four of her friends by members of the Manson Family in 1969.

Memories were still fresh of the Solar Temple massacres in Switzerland and Canada in the Autumn of 1994. Early the previous year there had been the startling saga which culminated in the firing of David Koresh's Branch Davidian compound in Waco, Texas. Going back further, in 1987 there had been the suspected murder-suicide pact of 33 followers of Park Soom Ja ("Benevolent Mother") whose bodies were found bound and gagged and neatly stacked in a South Korean factory attic.

Perhaps most notoriously of all, there was the mass deaths of members of the People's Temple in Jonestown, Guyana, in 1978.

That was a turning point in terms of the media projected image of such movements. Before, the press and television had treated them as harmless idiosyncratic groups of people marginalised on the outskirts of normal society. But media saturation following what became known succinctly as just "Jonestown" changed that. The label of "cult" was spread widely and indiscriminately over a variety of movements which the media lumped together in a single heavily stigmatized category. No attempt was made to distinguish one group from another.

Thus it was the word "cult" arrived upon the scene, with its derogatory overtones and trailing the baggage of association with all sorts of cruel and unnatural practices.

In academic circles these groups are known, in more objective-sounding parlance, as "new religious movements", or NRM's.

What, then, constitutes a NRM? According to Bryan Wilson[6] their defining characteristics are "exotic provenance; new cultural lifestyle; a level of engagement markedly different form that of traditional church Christianity; charismatic leadership; a following predominently young and drawn in disproportionate measure from the better-educated and middle-class sections of society; social conspicuity; international operation; and emergence within the last decade and a half."

Dr Eileen Barker, founder of INFORM - Information Network Focus on Religious Movements - describes NRM's as "alternative religions, non-conventional religions, cults or contemporary sects" and says that, depending on the definition used, there are currently around 500 of them in Britain.[7]

"In Britain," she says, "it is unlikely that any of the NRM's has succeeded, at any one time, in accumulating more than a few hundred members who devote their whole lives to working for their movement. It is impossible to estimate the number of people who, while living in their own homes and employed in "outside" jobs are deeply committed and devote almost all of their spare time to a particular group or movement ... If an estimate were to be made it would be likely to be somewhere in the tens of thousands. A greater number maintain a more peripheral relationship which may, none the less, be of considerable importance in their lives ... There could be a million or so people who have, minimally, dabbled in or flirted with one or other of the movements in Britain at some time during the past quarter century".

Like most unorthodox religious sects before them, cults have a tendency to live communally. In setting up their own communities they seek solitude from, or as a defence against a hostile world. Retreat into intentional communities ensures separation and isolation which provides protection for their ideals and beliefs. For other, less separatist sects, individuals and families find mutual support from living in communal households which are themselves intergrated rather than isolated from society. But there are many for whom communal living plays no part in their lives at all.

There are several hundred new religions which will include some sort of communal or collective living

The *Diggers and Dreamers* editors contacted Eileen Barker and asked her just how many cults practised communal living. She could give us no precise answer, but said: "There are several hundred new religions which will include some sort of communal or collective living."

She also added that some established sects, the Hare Krishna for example, were moving away from communal living, suggesting perhaps that as they feel more accepted, the protection offered by community, is felt less necessary. There are historical precedents for such trends with many old 'new religious movements' living in separate communities in their early days but abandoning it later. The best know example would be the Shakers. But there are also many examples of such sects surviving for several generations through their isolation in intentional communities. These include the Hutterites in America, and the Bruderhof in this country.

Some commentators sub-divide the NRM's into two categories: those which offer refuge and reform and those which offer to release people from conditions allegedly obstructing the full realisation of their human potential. Erhard Seminar Training (formerly known as "est"; now know as "Forum") and Transcendental Meditation (TM) would be two examples of the latter.

Dr Barker lists a sample of 40 different groups in an appendix to her Practical Introduction. They include the Unification Church (Moonies), International Society of Krishna Consciousness, Scientology, Divine Light Mission, Children of God /The Family, Church of Christ, Jesus Fellowship, Nichiren Shoshu and Rajneesh Foundation.

Societal changes in the wake of World War II produced the climate in which these movements have flourished. Vastly improved systems of communication and the resultant burgeoning of the mass media has increased the groups' visability and given access to wider potential market.

The post-war break down of society's consensual values and beliefs has created an ideal seed bed for the black-and-white certainties and unbending dogma which characterise many cults. Added to this, the baby boom between 1950 and 1965 produced large numbers of young adults in the 1970s and the ealy 1980s - the cohort from which membership of NRM's largely comes.

"Today's NRM's are novel in so far as they transcend the localized appeal and interest of earlier movements" say Beckford and Levesseur[8]. "This is clearly associated both with the central importance of young adults in NRM's and with the mass media's pre-occupation with such people."

Should we consider all cults/NRM's as sinister and potentially violent, exploitative and destructive? If one reads the tabloid press one might well believe that all of them are equally guilty of practices such as brainwashing or mind control, financial malpractice, greedy and power hungry leadership, sexual promiscuity, encouraging drug abuse, child abuse and, finally, hell-bent on mass murder and suicide.

No attempt is made to distinguish one cult or sect from another, despite the fact that they represent a wide spectrum of beliefs and practices, those of one group often being diametrically opposed to those of another

No attempt is made to distinguish one cult or sect from another, despite the fact that they represent a wide spectrum of beliefs and practices, those of one group often being diametrically opposed to those of another.

It is a common occurance to read tales of vulnerable young people being rescued from the clutches of some cult or other by one or several organisations - Christian Rescue, FAIR (Families Action Information Rescue), the Cult information Centre, and Catalist, for instance - set up for the purpose.

"There can be no non-violent relations between families and NRM's" assert Beckford and Levasseur. "The family defines itself as the victim of an attempt to missappropriate one of its offspring intended to keep the wider society going. Its role is to invest in education and thereby to reproduce a whole cultural system of which it is a trustee. By rejecting this role of living in a genealogical family, the sect member rejects the investment made in him or her and, as a result, in the family as well."

"Public opinion cannot understand this attitude so it can only talk in terms of abductions, black magic and brainwashing. It all has to do with the abduction of minors and families have met it with equal violence, as kidnappings and de-programmings have shown."

Indeed, if accusations of imprisonment and brain-washing can be levelled against cults, so they can against the so-called de-programmers. Accounts may be read of young people being confined against their will in a certain building, or even one room, until they are prepared to renounce their allegiance to their NRM. Their resistance may be worn down by sleep deprivation and constant bombardment with the truth as seen through the eyes of the anti-cultists. Much the same tactics, in fact, as those said by the rescuers to be employed by the offending cult hierarchies.

Perhaps the last word should be given to Dr Barker, whose organisation, INFORM, purports to research NRM's and provide "objective, balanced, up-to-date information". "Some of the movements have certainly been guilty of some ... malpractices," she says. "But the extent to which members of the NRM's are more likely than the rest of us to indulge in criminal or immoral practices has, on occasion, been grossly exaggerated. And the extent to which at least some of the members of some of the movements strive to lead more moral and spiritual lives than is usual in contemporary society tends to pass almost unrecognised."

Lee Jones is a founder member of the Quaker Community at Bamford in Derbyshire and also the mother of a former cult member. Having "retired" from social work in her early 50s to do an MA in Peace Studies at Bradford University, she now co-ordinates a community mediation service in Sheffield.

1 *Observer Magazine, Life* (14th, 21st, 28th May, 1995).
2 **Abrams, P & McCulloch, A** (1976) *Communes, Sociology and Society* Cambridge University Press, Cambridge.
3 **Ansell et al (eds)** (1989) *Diggers & Dreamers 1990/91* Communes Network, see pages 6 - 8.
4 ib id, p 7.
5 ib id, p 6.
6 **Wilson, B** (1981) *The Social Impact of New Religious Movements* Rose of Sharon Press, New York.
7 **Barker, E** (1989) *New Religious Movement: a Practical Introduction* HMSO.
8 **Beckford, J A and Levasseur, M** (1986) *New Religious Movements and Rapid Social Change* Sage Publications/UNESCO.

Vance G Martin writes: A Personal Remembrance of Peter Caddy. This article was first printed in the American magazine Communities and is reproduced with permission.

"... Boldness has Power, Magic and Genius In It ..."

Peter Caddy, Co-Founder of the Findhorn Foundation in Scotland, was a living embodiment of Goethe's timeless words, and his death was true to form. On 18 February 1994, Peter died instantly when a truck collided with his car near his home at Lake Constance, in southern Germany. Occurring just short of his 77th birthday (Peter was never accused of being "shy" of anything) the circumstances could only be called a collision, for, in Peter's world, there was "no such thing as an accident."

While best described as a leader and pioneer, Peter confounded stereotypes. I received an early lesson in this when, on my first day at Findhorn in 1974, I was asked to work in the kitchen and help prepare lunch for the 125 people (from 24 countries) then working in the Findhorn community. True to my own background in the American "consciousness movement," I proudly prepared one of my health food favorites, miso soup. A logical choice, I thought, to ward off the Scottish chill and to satisfy what had to be a health conscious community. Another person prepared a rich, cream soup, and another the salads.

The first person in the lunch queue was none other than the co-founder, Peter Caddy. As he picked up his bowl and addressed the soups, I leaned across the counter and spoke to him for the first time: "Peter, I've made a proper miso soup for you today." His astonishingly clear blue eyes pierced

through the steam rising from the soup kettle and, without missing a beat, he said, "I don't consider miso soup proper." He took the cream soup.

That was Peter - above all, an individual. With his wife Eileen and colleague Dorothy McLean, he led the Findhorn community and pioneered what became thc New Age movement by putting into practice a clearly defined world view based upon an individual's responsibility to follow their own higher purpose. The power of a person's positive thoughts, combined with obedience to their intuition (the divinity) within them, created enduring strength in a community. And, he constantly reminded us, a community needed to be constantly on guard not to become a "sausage machine," producing an endless chain of similar people.

From our perspective in the career and security-minded 1990s, Peter's life is a case-study in the time-tested virtues of flexibility, faith and hard work. After being the Command Catering Officer on the Burma front in  *the Royal Air Force, working at odd jobs around the UK (including being a Fuller Brush* salesman, door-to-door), and trans-forming a run down hotel into a four star hotel (with the daily divinely practical guidance received through Eileen), Peter ended up living in a tiny caravan (trailer) on a windy peninsula in northern Scotland, where he, Eileen, their three young sons, and Dorothy planted a small garden in the sand.

They were unaware of what would transpire ... an experiment in co-oper-ation between humankind and the Spirit of Nature, with profound results that has touched the hearts, inspired the dreams, and transformed the lives of countless people throughout the world. The subsequent story of what eventually became the Findhorn Foundation is well documented, including his own choice to eventually leave the community, separate from Eileen and, in his parting words, "go about my planetary work."

Whether it was in his attention to detail in cleaning toilets and weeding the gardens, his choice of soup, or in his love of the arts, Peter's participa-tion in all things was fueled by a cele-brated enjoyment of life's diversity and a boundless physical energy. But through it all, his blue eyes never wavered from "doing God's work." This was never more evident to me than in 1978 when we were on a lec-ture tour of Australia. On a visit to the beautiful coastline of southern Queensland, Peter insisted on jumping into the ocean. Not content with wad-ing, he body-surfed with abandon (at

60 years of age) until he was convinc-ingly slammed into the beach by a rogue wave. In acute pain, he stum-bled into his bed at the hotel, from which he gave numerous press inter-views, only to arise (gingerly) later that evening to present the Findhorn story to a sold-out audience. After this rest-ful holiday at the beach, we pressed on northwards the next day.

After hearing of Peter's passing, Kate and I shared with each other our memories and pictures of him, from 20 years of relationship: most recently with his (fifth) wife, Renara; hill-walk-ing in Scotland in the 1970s; crossing a glacier in New Zealand; and Peter at work in the Findhorn garden, radiat-ing energy while digging away. One could feel the nature spirits around him as he put his foot to the spade, helping to cultivate a New World.

Peter was a man of extraordinary achievement, as his life work attests. While always the center of attention and never far from controversy, he was saved from hubris by his wonder-ful ability to laugh at himself, and his constant adherence to a philosophy which was surprisingly uncomplicat-ed. Most importantly, he never looked down on anyone - he simply tried to understand their place in "the Plan."

By being destined - enthusiastically accepting the dare to traverse the edge of history, Peter Caddy faithfully fol-lowed his inner compass and thereby defined our times in a manner both singular and profound.

Vance Martin lived at Findhorn from 1974 until 1984. He served as Findhorn's Director of Garden and Environmental Programmes later as its Core-Group Focaliser and now is president of the International Wilderness Leadership (WILD) Foundation based in Colorado.

The end of the road to Utopia

ANDY WOOD

An overview of Intentional Communities from the Second World War to the early 1960s

The post war years were a barren time for communalism. In previous editions of Diggers and Dreamers, our historical series has shown that as a form of human association, communalism has a pedigree as long as Western civilisation itself. As a form of social dissent, the Utopian community has had a grand and notable tradition, for example: the Protestant sects of the middle ages and in the colonisation of the New World; the Utopian Socialism of Owen; the Kibbutsim of Israel.

In the 1994/5 edition we saw how communalism featured strongly in the social reformist ideas of the inter war years - notably with the Garden Cities and New Towns movement, but also in the land settlement movement which provided an avenue of dissent for war resisters during the World War II.

A great many of these ideas were adopted and then adapted by the State in a variety of ways as the welfare system was planned and then implemented immediately after the war. Policies on new towns and green belts made garden cities and back-to-the-land redundant; commitment to Keynsian economics, unemployment benefits and state pensions did away with the need of land colonies for the unemployed; a national health service even made the successful and revolutionary Peckham Health Centre experiment obsolete. The war brought a great deal of social unity and need for major rebuilding of the social and economic as well as physical fabric of society. A landslide Labour victory heralded a period in which utopian thinking, in a way, became Government policy. Commentators like Armytage in 'Heavens Below'[1], could sit back and assess the influence of utopian thought on State policy. For some it was a time to deride the antiquated efforts of previous communalists; and for others

Diggers & Dreamers 1947/48! Information extracted from the Community Broadsheet - an occasional collection of Community News produced by something called the Community Services Committee in the immediate post war years. There are communities, in some form, at the places listed below to this day (although the Bruderhof have moved).

Iona, by Oban
"The tasks and opportunities ... continue to expand ... This year the resident summer community numbers 18"

Lee Abbey, Lynton, Devon
"Groups of 10 or 15 people from different parishes ... will come with one of their clergy. The aim is to get them spiritually on fire ..."

Othona, Bradwell-juxta-Mare, Essex
"A one week conference was held during July ... to discuss plans for 1948 and the significance of Othona in relation to the whole community movement ..."

St Julian's, Barns Geen, Sussex
"We are now a much larger concern, and the time of experimenting is, in some degree, over. We have consolidated and we have learnt much."

Taena, Lydney, Gloucestershire
"... we believe in in the building up of many sided, balanced, 'village'

community life ... it will grow organically and spontaneously like a tree in response to the earth and sun and rain - or it will wither and die. Which it is to be is at any moment only determined by the inner response which each individual makes to life within."

Thelnetham, Diss, Norfolk
"Of the original group which came ... to Thelnetham in 1942, practically nobody remains. There has been almost an entire turnover of personnel ... Are men willing to work hard enough ... to support themselves? In a community-farm the stark problem of modern morality stares one simply in the face. No amount of idealistic highfalutin' can disguise it."

Wheathill Bruderhof, Bridgnorth, Salop
"We are continuing mixed farming on our 532 acres of land ... The surplus of our products, after supplying our household of 120 (including children) is sold ... we invite you to come and live and work and seek with us"

to lament its passing. All in all however, the road to utopia was concluded to be at an end, for good or worse.

Few commentators on communal living in this time would have predicted the resurgence of it as a major form of social dissent which followed in the late Sixties. But if they had looked closely enough, they would have perhaps seen that the seeds were not dead, but merely hibernating.

> "... Utopia was justified on sheerly practical grounds, as a retreat from atomic warfare, a summer-vacation colony, a novelty in personal relations; and though in their hearts they too hoped for some millenial outcome of the experiment, for the reign of justice and happiness, they shrank from a definition of the colony which committed them to any positive belief. Conspicuous goodness, like the Founder's filled them with uneasy embarrassment; they looked upon it as a form of simple-mindedness on a par with vegetarianism, and would have refused admission to Heaven on the ground that it was full of greenhorns and cranks."
>
> From Mary McCarthy's "A Source of Embarrasment". Published in 1950, Punch described it as a "smooth, deadly account of an American Utopian community" containing "fiendishly precise description and criticism of the varieties and holders of 'advanced' opinion."

In the Bohemian circles of the Beat Generation one could probably have found the antecedents of the hippy crash pads - collective living of the 'quasi-communal' type so inelloquently described by Abrams and Mc-Culloch[2]. The charismatic appeal of mystics and other non conformist religious sects did, as they always have, give rise to the communal group here and there. Coombe Springs (see page 72) was thus inspired by Gurdjieff. After settling and then abandoning communities in southern England in between the Wars, the German originating Bruderhof re-established their community in the Ludlow area, and have subsequently thrived elsewhere.

Some authors were taking a new look at the theraputic possibilities of collective living for the mentally ill and people with learning dufficulties. Rudolph Steiner put this into practice with his Camphill communities (page 85). Also during this

time psychiatrist B F Skinner wrote his utopian novel
Walden Two which was to become the inspiration
of Twin Oaks - a flag ship community of the modern era. Other groups too were rediscovering the simple social and economic benefits of sharing (see The
Beginnings of Braziers, page 76).

So whilst Iris Murdoch in 'The Bell'[3], was
able to capitalise on the unpopularity of
the utopian effort, communalism was
kept alive in these nooks and crannies of
society, until it was ready to burst forth upon
the popular consiousness once again just
a few years later.

"... Utopia was justified on sheerly practical grounds, as a retreat from atomic warfare, a summer-vacation colony, a novelty in personal relations; and though in their hearts they too hoped for some millenial outcome of the experiment, for the reign of justice and happiness, they shrank from a definition of the colony which com-mitted them to any positive belief. Conspicuous goodness, like the Founder's filled them with uneasy embarrassment; they looked upon it as a form of simple-mindedne "And the colony itself ... with its energy, its uncertainty, its euphoria, its cycles of recession and recovery, seemed also to have been prismatically imaging the galvanic world down below - in the social field, it had been treating itself as a kind of factory or business for the manufacture and export of morality. The spirits of the colonists rose and fell with the market-quotation of the enterprise; at the moment, its stock was very low. These crises ... would shake the colony to pieces, unless a new pattern were discovered ... But it might survive ... if the production of a commodity more tangible than morali-ty could be undertaken. Morality did not keep well; it required stable condi-tions; it was costly; it was subject to variations, and the market for it was uncertain."

From Mary McCarthy's "A Source of Embarrasment".

1 **Armytage, W H G** (1961) *Heavens Below: Utopian Experiments in England 1560 - 1960* Routledge and Kegan Paul, London. See the Epilogue for his commentary and what others thought of utopianism at that time. These include novelists Iris Murdoch and Aldous Huxley, philosophers Karl Popper, Erich Fromm and Karl Mannheim, Sociologist C Wright Mills and social historian G D H Cole.

2 **Abrams, P and McCulloch, A** (1976) *Communes, Sociology and Society* Cambridge University Press, Cambridge.

3 **Murdoch, I** (1958) *The Bell* is about a community occupied by "a kind of sick people whose desire for God makes them unsatisfactory citizens of an ordinary life, but whose strengths or temperament fails them to surrender the world completely."

Gurdjieff Movements in Leafy Surrey

ANGELA BARKER

George Ivanovitch Gurdjieff was a Russian who claimed to have been in contact with a secret brotherhood in Asia. His community near Paris was once described as 'a mixture of monastery, labour camp and mad hatter's tea party'. After World War II a British disciple of Gurdjieff, set up a community in which his ideas might be put into practice. This was life at Coombe Springs in the 1950s.

During the war, John G Bennett, a former pupil at the Château du Prieuré (Gurdjieff's institute in France), was working as a government scientist investigating the efficient use of coal. By the early 1940s, his department had made its headquarters at a seven acre country estate near London, known as Coombe Springs. There he, as head of department, managed to also invite small groups of people, from time to time, for the continuance of the Gurdjieff work. At the end of the war he was able, together with others, to buy the property where he then founded The Institute for the Comparitive Study of History, Philosophy and the Sciences. It was behind this rather forbidding title that the Coombe Community grew and flourished, providing some of us who were too young to have met and worked with Gurdjieff an opportunity to gain experience from those who had, creating, as it were, a 'second generation' school.

Perhaps the stickiest problem facing those who seek to direct an establishment of this kind is that of ensuring that the teaching does not stand still. It must be ongoing and has to be made to suit not only the current social climate but also each individual, according to need. It is important to note that Gurdjieff did not preach a doctrine, nor try to establish anything resembling a 'belief system'. He taught both a psychology and a cosmology in a form that could be assimilated by each pupil in his or her own way. The job of the school is, therefore, to provide a place where conditions are created for the individual to learn, rather than a building in which knowledge is dispensed.

"Discussion at the house meetings was confined to whether or not the applicant would benefit from becoming a resident"

Such were the problems facing J G Bennett when he became the Director of the Coombe Community. At the outset, he gained some measured approval from Gurdjieff who, at the end of the war, had re-emerged in Paris. Bennett had been well taught and several hundred people regularly attended various events at Coombe, in addition to the thirty or so in residence. A number of building projects were undertaken, the most ambitious being that of an assembly hall. This turned out to be nine-sided and approximately 60 feet both in height and breadth.

The inspiration for the hall was derived from Bennett's observations and measurements of a dervish tekke, or sema hane (house of blessing), which he had known well when he lived in Turkey. It took some six years to build and utilised a number of skills possessed by members of the Institute. Only one person involved in the building work came from outside the larger community; he was the driver of the crane, hired for the final capping of the roof. Probably the most fascinating aspect of the construction process was that it took place without any formal design. It was, as it were, extemporised. The Community's architecture group (of about 15 professional architects) built a model 'after the fact' and attended to the details of building technique, etc. By 1960 the hall stood in the grounds at Coombe like a giant, nine-sided pepperpot - it was named The Djamichunatra.

The life at Coombe Springs was not quite so arduous as that at the Paris institute. The first morning exercise took place at 7.00am in the 'Djami'. Breakfast followed this, after which the residents who worked 'outside' departed and those who remained set about those tasks necessary for the running of an estate. After lunch, work continued until the 'outside' workers returned and the entire household asembled for dinner. Then there would be classes in the rhythmic movements, or meetings of various sub-groups whose numbers would be swelled by visitors from London or nearby Kingston upon Thames.

The Djamich-unatra, "a nine sided pepperpot", at Coombe Springs in Surrey

Every other weekend would include a 'Work Sunday' which, in addition to the ongoing work programme, served as the means by which new people were introduced to the community. Applicants for residency were expected to have attended several Work Sundays prior to their cases being raised at one of the house meetings, held regularly on Tuesday evenings. They might also have chosen to stay as temporary residents for a weekend, or simply overnight, so that the indigenous community would come to know them reasonably well. Discussion at the house meetings was confined to whether or not the applicant would benefit from becoming a resident. Since the applicant had already shown his or her propensities, rejections were rare. The candidate's sex, nationality or cultural background were of no consequence in this selection. In fact, the broader the cross-section of society that was represented, the better this was considered to be. The accommodation could have been either in the main house or one of a number of outbuildings. These included a large, prefabricated condominium known, for some reason, as 'The Fishbowl'.

As an institute, Coombe Springs provided the base for a number of loosely related research projects including the experimental educational ideas of Dr Maria Montessori; 'Systematics' - Bennett's logical extension of Gurdjieff's cosmology; and Subud - a spiritual exercise from Indonesia. It was Subud which was to give rise to a major schism in the Institute and those who felt that it was an affront to Gurdjieff's teaching left. When, eventually, the original routine of the community was re-established, a few returned.

Coombe Springs closed down in 1966 under circumstances which, in retrospect, seem to have been, to say the least, bizarre. Of the seven acre estate only the lodge now remains, the rest having been demolished to make way for rather distasteful stockbroker-belt residences. Bennett moved to Gloucestershire where he opened a new institute, based on his own presumed extension of Gurdjieff's ideas. He died in December 1974.

Angela Barker was in touch with Coombe Springs from 1958 to 1966 and lived there for just over five years. She now lectures in mythology, symbology and metaphysics and lives on the river with her partner, Richard, and two dogs.

The Beginnings of Braziers

DOROTHY GLAISTER

Founded after WWII, Braziers' origins go back to the early 1920s.

This is an edited version of the personal recollections of the late

Dorothy Glaister. Her marriage to Harley Street psychiatrist

Norman Glaister had guaranteed the kind of life that was highly

unusual in the 1950s. She wrote this description in the early 70s.

Soon after the end of the First World War a group of younger members of the "No More War" organisation came to the conclusion that it was the particular job of the young to live together and prove practically that war would be impossible if people had a positive relationship towards each other. Many years later one of their number, Norman Glaister, took these ideas a stage further by initiating an experiment in which a body of people were willing and anxious to make a success of their life together.

Norman and his secretary scoured the countryside and after one visit to a house in Oxfordshire they reported back to the others that they had found what Norman described as "Such a funny house". It was Braziers. The price was far beyond us so they went on seeking. Then one day Norman received a letter from the owner saying that he was willing to sell at our price, since he would like his old home to be used for educational purposes. It was decided that the community should earn its living as a "Residential Adult Education Centre".

Norman, Glyn Faithfull (another member of the group who had met Norman through "The Order of Woodcraft Chivalry" more than a quarter of a century earlier) and others should run the courses, inviting other outside lecturers and course-takers to join them. The rest of the community were to run the household, garden, kitchen, library etc.

In November 1950 Braziers was officially opened by Mr Farquharson, founder of the Sociological Society. Among the early subjects of study for weekend courses were: The Hypothesis of Extra-Sensory Perception", and "The Herd Psychology of Politics".

It is not easy to settle down in a countryside where one is not known. The village found understanding us at first a tough nut to crack. We were variously believed by some of them to be either nudists or communists. However we managed to live that down with the help of the village shop-keeper and others who came to know us. Several of the women joined the local branch of the Women's Institute and later Glyn and some other members of the community ran the village Youth Club. But life was hard in the early days. Food was still rationed and we had to economise with food during the weekdays so as to have a reasonable supply of good quality food during the weekend courses. Mains electricity was not available to us at first, so we continued to make our own from a generator in an outbuilding. It was quite an event for us when mains electricity became available.

> **"We were variously believed by some of them to be either nudists or communists"**

Material affairs continued to be very difficult. We came near to the end of our resources. Our lawyer advised us to close down. But Norman had a theory, which some of us shared, that if an enterprise is worth while it will not close solely for financial reasons, but only if it fails spiritually. The more stalwart of us backed him up in this.

The First Schism

We had some very difficult meetings. Norman put it before us that he had no more money to put into Braziers, and asked that some of the rest of us would share the burden. Some did, but there was not enough. The suggestion was made that the management should be entirely changed. There was a silence in the meeting. The point of view of the dissidents was that if they could run it more as an arts centre they could make it pay. The meeting was adjourned.

When we met again the dissidents had decided not to press their point. What was more they all retired from membership. The prospect was bleak, but we beleived that we had something to give that people needed and that somehow we would succeed.

The Farm

At about this time Norman decided that the whole enterprise needed a farm attached to it. Between Braziers Farm and Braziers School of Integrative Social Research there was to be a quid-pro-quo arrangement whereby Braziers lent labour to the farm and the farm lent machinery to Braziers. Also the farm would give priority in the sale of its produce to Braziers at a sum below the market rate. Norman suggested that I might produce the capital to stock the farm out of the sale of some of my industrial shares. My first reaction was "I think we ought to keep my shares for use in setting up our boys to earn their living. Besides I don't want to be a farmer - I'm too old. If you had asked me 20 years ago I would have loved it." He countered that by saying "I'll do all that is necessary - I'll be farm manager, and if the farm does not prove a success, we can always sell the machinery and animals."In the end I consented. So a trained farm worker came. He had to be paid a farm worker's wage (albeit the minimum), which was about three times as much as the community honorarium. Twelve milk cows were bought and a tractor. We had a milking parlour. Corn was sown in the fields to make straw and fodder for the cows, and the farm was set up. Later on, difficulties arose (financial and other), our farm worker left us, and after accepting temporary help from some others I passed the leasehold of the farm over to Glynn with a "gentleman's agreement" between us that in any year when he made any profit on the farm I should be paid 4% on the capital. It was making no profit at all when Glynn took over. In fact it was in debt.

The Second Schism

Then came another schismatic process. It seemed to be the result of two totally different causes. There was an unmarried Chinese girl working with us who was expecting a baby, and Norman decided that it would be best for her and the child and Braziers if she went elsewhere to have the child. Some people wanted to take care of her here and considered that it would be terribly callous of us to, as they put it, "turn her out". No one wanted to "turn her out" but to find a suitable mother and baby home for her to go to. Still others of us felt that to preside over the advent of a baby was not within the scope of an Adult Education Centre. At the same time we were still struggling to make ends meet without much success and someone suggested that the

Braziers Park near Wallingford in Oxon - a fine example of Strawberry Hill Gothic and "such a funny house"

financial management should be placed in the hands of two financially efficient people who offered their services. It was feared by Norman that such an arrangement on the financial side might lead eventually to sacrificing the main objects for which Braziers stood and we continued to believe that the objects for which we stood were really needed by people and that people in sufficient numbers would eventually be anxious to take part in and pay for courses which might throw some light on mankind and its future development, etc.

Most of us felt that this aim was even more important than the financial objective, so we said "No thank you" to our friends who offered to give us their help and went on with our struggle. Some of our number (not members but workers on the houseteam) were inclined to think we were wrong in this decision, and at the same time were disappointed in us for wanting the Chinese girl to have her baby in a different place. They decided to leave us, and we were left to run the place without a houseteam except those of us who were also members of Braziers - that meant without the farmer, the gardener, the cook, the handiman, the book-keeper, and the principal worker in the house. It left Norman, Bonnie and I with the help of two village girls. Glynn did what he could at week-ends and holidays, but as he was a lecturer at Liverpool University he had a long way to commute. However, he worked on the farm, sawed up the wood on the circular saw as well as taking courses. We had saved our objective once again, but had lost good people.

To return to the result of our second schism, Glynn said that next time when a schism appears about to take place we must learn to pursue the schismatic process courageously and co-operatively, but to stop short of schism, and to continue to do so till we (both sides) reach an acceptable synthesis. We felt that this, however obvious it seems to us now, may be one of the main results of the practical side of our research, perhaps the first little step towards seeing our way to the avoidance of wars???

These two schisms have been described at length because one of the main objectives of our life and work here is to try to discover how to cope with schism. In other words we need to find out how to integrate opposites - whether these opposites are opposite points of view, opposite capacities, different ideals or merely a clash of temperaments. In the cases I have described we did not integrate the two opposites. Instead, a break was made and one side walked out. That denotes a failure.

Student Helpers

We had long ago rejected the idea of a two-class society, and we now saw that the process of finding people who wanted to join our community and take part in promoting its work of learning and teaching was a very slow one (and rightly so).

The solution was suggested by the lecturer in English at a teachers' training college in Germany. He asked if we would like to take some of his students to work with us and at the same time to learn English. We accepted. From then on we have opened a temporary membership of our community to young men and women from abroad who wanted to have practice in speaking English and were willing to work and live with us for a few weeks or months. Our week-end courses are open to them, as to us, as far as catering for our visitors and ourselves allows. Now we are a community with a continually changing number of young temporary members from all over the world. We learn from them as well as them from us.

The Studies House Meeting

In any group activity of mind or body or spirit, a sine-qua-non is communication of some sort. Every community needs to find its own way of helping to bring this about. It is not just friendly chat that is needed though friendly chat certainly has its place. The possibility of a deeper sharing of thoughts, ideas and personal problems is one of the attractions of living in community. One cannot organise such communication, but one can pave the way for it to take place. The need to communicate in depth comes to every one at times. It comes more easily to some than to others but it can be facilitated by atmosphere and by custom. Each community will find its own best means of ensuring that its members have the opportunity of communicating and being communicated with. Glynn invented one of our ways of making this possible. Every Sunday evening when the work of the week-end is over and we have tidied up the place somewhat and are beginning to sit back in our chairs we have a trolley supper together in the inner hall (by a big log fire in the winter). When supper is over and washed up, we sit around in a circle, and first we have a round consisting of each of us saying something we have learnt during the week. We can always say "Pass" when our turn comes round if we have not learnt anything, or we cannot remember what we have learnt, or do not wish to share it. Our very varied contributions usually lead to much general conversation and the sharing of knowledge and information. Next we have a round of what we call "problem-facing". In turn we can tell the others of any problem we may have or that the community has, and they can give any suggestions they think may be helpful for its solution. Or, if we have no problem, we can ask a question, or again We can just "pass". We find this a helpful means of sharing our concerns with each other and keeping in touch, sometimes deeply.

The Quiet Meeting
We have another kind of meeting on Sunday mornings, which we call the "Quiet Meeting". It is a meeting for prayer and/or thought and/or meditation. It is structured rather like a meeting of the "Society of Friends". Any person who feels he or she has some thought to express, which may be of value to the others also, can express it. An interval of silence is left after each contribution to the thought of the meeting so that there may be time for the listeners to take in fully what has been said. The idea is for people to accept what they can of the thought expressed and to build on that in their own mind. Negative criticism is not suitable on such occasions. We aim rather to build together and clarify the

thought of the meeting. Argument and discussion, as such, are avoided .

Our Philosophy
It was not ours - it was drawn from the thoughts of many great minds. A number of us began with a simple kind of Christian philosophy. Others of us were humanists probably with a predominantly Christian ethic. But what drew us together and set us further on our way was Wilfred Trotter's idea of a multi-mental organism as expressed in his book *Instincts of the Herd in Peace and War* - that, and the very patent fact that some alternative would have to be found for the habit of drifting towards war which the so-called civilised nations of the world seemed to have formed. A correspondence started in the *Sunday Times*, led by Julian Huxley on the subject of "The Destiny of Man". One of our members, John Murrell, entered into it, mentioning our name, and the result was a pile of letters to our secretary, and some new members, including John Woodcock, and later also his wife Evelyn. They became members, not of the group of people living at Braziers, but of the larger company of people called members, who worked with us in thought and spirit. Some of these, formed a communal household in London. All their members went out to work but shared their home and much of their thoughts.

The next great light which influenced our thought came from Teilhard de Chardin. His *Phenomenon of Man* seemed to many of us as an expression in poetry of a great and complicated scientific fact which led up to man in his present state of evolution and might, with sufficient understanding, lead beyond man. I have omitted to mention the great religious and philosophical leaders of the distant past whose underlying influence was perhaps greatest of all. Looking back over the last 20-plus years one wonders what is the chief contribution we have made to the noosphere (to use Teilhard's term for the knowing-thinking-spiritual part of the universe). I would guess that perhaps it lies in the tiny step forward which this (and I think and hope some other groups) have made in the direction of "thinking together", not by sinking our own individual contribution and giving in to a mere majority, but by contributing any original thought-feeling we may have and building it in (or integrating it with) the deliberative thought-feeling of the whole group. So far, people working together in a group tend to withdraw from the group when they do not see eye-to-eye with it. It is difficult not to do so. We regard withdrawal as failure to do what we have all set out to do together, namely to create a group capable, of more comprehensive thought and knowledge and action than any one individual can be. To meet creatively with differences, even fundamental differences, within the group is one of the big problems - perhaps the main problem - that confronts us today in the making of our group mind, and of our co-ordinated world.

Dorothy Glaister was one of the early Fabians. She was closely involved with the progressive school movement and, later, the Committee of 100. She lived at Braziers for the last 30 years of her life and died there in 1981.

The community at Braziers thrives to this day. Their Directory entry is on page 183.

Care in the Community?

VIVIAN GRIFFITHS

A short history of the Camphill Movement.

L iving in community is a common bond which unites the communes movement with the many communities of intention , whose work is grounded in common social or religious beliefs. This can be a monastery or a village community with people with special needs - or even a house community in an urban setting working with some of the social challenges of our time.

It is this common bond of community living which links the Camphill Communities to other communities in the pages of *Diggers and Dreamers*. For those who come as co-workers to Camphill, this living in community is more than merely helping to do good or pursuing a career as a professional carer. Central to this is the equality of living and working with children and adults with special needs - a common experience, struggles, joys and all, of communes and communities alike.

In 1995 the Camphill Communities are 55 years old: 1940 saw the start of the Camphill Rudolf Steiner Schools. The story begins with the arrival in 1938-9 of a group of refugees from Austria after the occupation of their country. The doctor who had asked for permission to come - Dr Karl König - was offered a house in Scotland for this group and in the midst of war these people whose main language was that of the so-called enemy started a school. This community school established near Aberdeen was able to take a number of children with special needs, some from families caught up in the persecution of war who had to move from Europe to America.

The Camphill Schools were from the start communities of sharing. Not only the sharing of the common tasks of school and domestic life but also of the philosophy and ideals of Anthroposophy. Rudolf Steiner's Curative Education Course, which had been given to a group of teachers and doctors looking after children with special needs in a special home in 1924, formed the cornerstone of the community school. The beginnings of the modern thought that people with disabilities could be part of special education and social rehabilitation and become active citizens with a family life and jobs in the community had begun.

After the war the Camphill Rudolf Steiner Schools played a small but significant part in the reconstruction of the relationship between Britain and Germany which saw young people coming from Middle Europe to the school and helping to establish new Camphill Communities in Thornbury near Bristol, Ringwood in the New Forest and in Northern Ireland on Belfast Lough.

In the 1950s the parents of the original children of the Camphill Schools, while waiting for their children coming on the overnight train in a waiting room in King's Cross station, started talking. They had plenty of time because the train was often late! The main topic was the future of their offspring. In a series of meetings with the founder Dr Karl König in the Magic Circle Club in London the idea was born of a land and craft village community with adult people with special needs, and forty years ago in September 1955 the first settlement of its kind was established on the North Yorkshire Moors at Botton. For Camphill co-workers it was a matter of learning all over again the skills of community, with equality between adults: the establishment of working life in the farms, craft workshops and households. There was also a hope that the parents who

had been so involved in the meetings with Dr König would take up the challenge and come to live in the community. It was not to be, apart from a few notable exceptions, and instead the first of the active friends support groups was established.

Meanwhile Camphill Communities were also being established in other countries. Requests from America and South Africa, and the beginnings in Germany and Norway can be traced to the early 1960s. And across the Irish Sea, the Glencraig Trust in Northern Ireland established its first school and village at the same time as Botton. It was the first of a network of communities both north and south of the border with a unique relationship to the two nations of Ireland.

Having established schools and villages Camphill co-workers, parents and friends increasingly noticed the yawning gap of need that existed between childhood and adulthood for the disabled person. This need was often remarked on by parents or interested people employed in a social services or edu-

Worshipping together is an important part of life together for villagers and co-workers at Camphill communities. This is Newton Dee Village Community Chapel.

A House Community at the Loch Arthur Village Community, Dumfries & Galloway

cation department, and to answer it there were established training centres and colleges for adolescents in Sussex, central Scotland and in the town of Kendal in the Lake District. In countries where a school had been established, these colleges for teenagers and later young adults began. These new centres of learning of primary experiences in craft and land work offered a community life to more and more disadvantaged young people, who benefited enormously from the experiences of a different environment away from sometimes uncreative home situations.

Many of the Camphill Communities are in a rural setting. It was the demand for a more independent and yet supportive environment that brought about the first urban community in Stourbridge, then in north Worcestershire, in 1969. This community in a town which developed slowly, became an important blueprint when two local authorities asked for a Camphill Community in their midst in the 1980s. The Milton Keynes Development Corporation, looking for more diversity in their new-town community, invited the setting up of a Camphill Community there. In Middlesbrough in the north east of England, the town council who were concerned at the huge unemployment levels as old industries closed, invited the Camphill Village Trust to start a community on a farm on the edge of the town. This farm provides the nucleus of a workshop, market garden and a training guild whereby local people could set up craft businesses in return for taking on people with special needs in their training programme.

The integration into the wider community has been a feature of the more recent history of Camphill. Closer relationships with social services departments, more involvement with parents and friends, and the wealth of new regulations and laws which Camphill has to be aware of means that the interface of the community with the so-called world has had to change out of all recognition. This reflects changes in the aspirations of the communities, which wish this interaction. Gone are the days when co-workers joined the community to turn their back on a troubled world even for a few years. Now a more integrated approach is the norm.

Villagers at work in the Grange Village Community Pottery

Yet the need for a supportive environment, a so-called island of healing, in a community for all comers has never been so important, and Camphill has striven to maintain this. There is a certain destiny involved in coming to live in a Camphill Community, yet all people who approach are warmly considered and welcomed.

Vivian Griffiths has been a co-worker in Camphill communities since the mid-1970s. He has lived at Botton Village and Larchfield Community in Middlesbrough and is now working on a land-based project for the Camphill Houses Urban Community in Stourbridge.

Walter Segal: Community Architect

COLIN WARD

The name of the late Walter Segal is now synonymous with Self-Build Housing but few know that Walter, himself, was raised in a Bohemian commune in Bohemia!

Whenever people meet to discuss what they could do to house themselves, someone mentions the Segal system of quickly-built, timber-framed dwellings which are environmentally friendly, and seem to generate friendship among the self-build groups that have succeeded in housing themselves this way. The attraction increases when we learn that they include men and women with every kind of disadvantage, including poverty, age and disablement, and that they often say that the experience changed their lives.

The heartbreaks and delays that self-builders experience are not to do with the process of building itself, but, as Walter Segal used to observe, are the result of the inflated price of land, the rigidities of planning and building controls, and the difficulty of getting mortgage loans for anything out of the ordinary. They are all made worse by the assumption of both regulatory authorities and providers of finance, that a house should be a full-finished product right from the start, rather than a simple basic structure that grows over time as needs grow and as labour and income can be spared. Segal's achievement was to devise a way of simplifying the process of building so that it could be undertaken by anyone, cheaply and quickly. He insisted that his was an approach, not a system, and he made no claims for originality or patents.

The Segal approach was essentially that of the medieval English house, or the American frame-house, or the Japanese house, but with the timber frame calculated and based on modular dimensions to avoid waste and to facilitate alterations and enlargements. He sought to elim-

Walter Segal: In his life, as well as his work, he tried to pare away the superfluous and concentrate on the important

inate or reduce the 'wet trades' of concreting, bricklaying and plastering, by reducing the sheer weight of the building, and by using cladding, insulating and lining materials in their standard sizes. In his life, as well as his work, he tried to pare away the superfluous and concentrate on the important.

My purpose is not to describe the Segal method, but to recount the effect on his life and personality of growing up in an anarchist commune, and his evolution late in life, as the architect, friend and advisor of community self-builders.

The boy from the commune
Walter's parents were Jewish Romanians who met in Berlin, where his father, an expressionist painter, was taking part in an exhibition of the group called the New Secession. He was born in 1907 and in 1914 the family moved to the hills above Ascona in the Swiss canton of Ticino. There, in 1900, a colony had been started, trying, as Walter explained, "to find

a new meaning in life," and was called Monte Verita, the Mountain of Truth. Like the aspirations of, say, Whiteway Colony in Gloucestershire, or Edward Carpenter's hopes of new communities around Sheffield, it was a revolt against the appalling stuffiness, in clothing, diet and means of livelihood of the atmosphere of the late 19th century. Monte Verita was founded by Henri Oedenkoven, a Fleming from Antwerp, and Karl Grüser, from the German minority in Hungary, whose younger brother Gustav, wandering through Germany "with long hair, sandals and bare legs" was met by the writer Hermann Hesse, who followed him down to the colony and spent most of his life there. It figures in the lives of many subsequently famous writers, painters and revolutionaries.

They rejected convention in marriage and dress, party politics and dogmas: they were tolerantly intolerant

Segal's recollections are like those of many children reared in alternative communities: "The colonists abhorred private property, practised a rigid code of morality, strict vegetarianism and nudism. They rejected convention in marriage and dress, party politics and dogmas: they were tolerantly intolerant." He reflected that "To have spent childhood and adolescence in an environment of artists, architects, writers, life-reformers, thinkers and truthseekers, ideologues and mystics, charlatans and cranks, many of whom have left their mark upon our time - and unfortunately perhaps, continue to do so - was in a way a singular piece of good luck; but there were moments when I longed for ordinariness and went to seek it."

He found it among the village children, untrammelled by seriousness. "So I had playmates in both camps which meant that I was affected by the lives of both the Bohemians and the ordinary philistines. And I have since found myself all the time moving from one camp to the other, never really able to adjust to one world only." He was an outdoor child and

realised early in life that his work
was to be in building. "So I gradually slid into an understanding of how
buildings are put up, and it was clear
to me by the age of fourteen that I
was going to be an architect." And
he was fortunate in picking up an
American house-carpenter's manual
on the ordinary American tradition of
'balloon-frame' building of houses
and barns.

The family were living in poverty,
but suddenly a patron appeared for the
painter Arthur Segal in the form of a
rich anarchist sympathiser, Bernhard
Mayer, and Walter was enabled to
study architecture among the pio-
neers of the Modern Movement in
Delft, Berlin and Paris. In Berlin, learning from engineers he resolved that
"every building I was going to make,
I would calculate" and he won a schol-
arship to finish his education at the
Technical High School in Zurich. "In
Switzerland I learned one very important thing: joinery. I learned it very well indeed."

Houses in
Deya (mal-
lorca)
drawn by
Walter
Segal in
1934

In 1932 he was commissioned by the same Bernhard
Mayer to build a little wooden holiday cabin, La Casa
Piccola, at Ascona. It is still standing and has many
of the characteristics of the Segal-style houses that
self-build co-operatives are putting up in Britain today.
"I went back to Ascona to build," Segal recalled,
"It became clear to me that one can have a small
path and tread it alone." He was undoubtedly
shaped by his commune childhood. The architectural critic Peter Blundell Jones was right in saying that "At Monte Verità Walter saw enough
artistic self-indulgence to last a lifetime," but he was
also right in perceiving that "Walter was already
steeped in far too rich and broad a culture and had
become too much of a lone wolf ever to join any pack.
He had to find his own way in everything, and con-
fessed that he could never submit to authority."

Hard times and a happy accident

He came to London in 1936, teamed up with Eva Bradt, a student from the Architectural Association School, and scraped a living on the fringe of the architectural world, during and after the second world war, writing prolifically in the trade journals and teaching at the Architectural Association School. As housing was bound to be a key post-war issue, he wrote a massive book "Home and Environment" (Leonard Hill 1948, 1953) and another on an issue which is more topical today than it was then, "Planning and Transport: Their Effects on Industry and Residence" (Dent, for the Co-operative Permanent Building Society 1945). Books bring prestige but not an income, and the post-war building boom passed him by. A handful of well-connected left-wing architects had a huge output of housing and schools. They would not have taken seriously the small jobs that came his way: little buildings in Hackney for the Premium Pickle Company or a small office for Tretol Ltd and a few self-generated housing projects.

Professional rejection meant nothing to him. He had a happy family life, was incredibly well-read in several European languages and was a familiar figure in the architecture schools. I first met him when I went to talk at one of them and found a knot of students towering over a small, round, twinkling man pouring out a stream of paradoxes in a very soft voice. And his subsequent fame came by accident. Eva died in 1950 and a decade later Walter and a new partner Moran Scott, with six children between them, decided to demolish and rebuild their home at Highgate and to put up a temporary house at the bottom of the

> **The lightweight timber structure, with no foundations other than paving slabs, and using standard cladding materials and linings in market sizes (so that they could be re-used elsewhere) took two weeks to build and cost £800**

garden to live in meanwhile. The lightweight timber structure, with no foundations other than paving slabs, and using standard cladding materials and linings in market sizes (so that they could be re-used elsewhere) took two weeks to build and cost £800.

Walter Segal with a group of self-builders at Lewisham

It is there to this day, snug as ever. I remember sleeping in it when it was only twenty years old, with deep snow all around. Visitors to the Segals were more interested in the little house in the garden than in their new house on the street front. It led to a series of commissions up and down the country for houses built on the same principle, with Walter refining and improving the method every time. A carpenter, Fred Wade, followed him from site to site, and everywhere the clients were able to do more and more of the building themselves, varying the plans to suit their needs and make additions.

By the mid-1970s, as the crisis of confidence in local authority housing deepened, Walter was yearning to find one council that would sponsor a build-it-yourself experiment of this kind for people on its housing waiting or transfer list. Eventually, by one vote, the London Borough of Lewisham decided to do so, on pockets of land too small, awkward or sloping, to fit its own building programme. There were two and a half years of agonising delay, simply because the proposal didn't fit the standard ways of financing, providing or controlling buildings, but in the end it happened.

Everyone involved was delighted. Ken Atkins of the Lewisham Self-Build Housing Association reflected on what he called the "indescribable feeling that you finally have control over what you are doing." And Segal himself, in the context of the universal gloom hanging over housing in Britain - was overjoyed to have helped to prove in the most convincing way imaginable "that there is among the people that live in this country such a wealth of talent." He found it unbelievable that this creativity would continue to be denied an outlet.

The Segal legacy
Walter died, aged 78, in October 1985. Within the architectural world his role had shifted from that of a loner and outsider to that of a moral force both inside and outside the profession. He is the only contemporary architect to have two roads named after him: Segal Close and Walter's Way, tokens of the affection he inspired among self-builders. When I last talked to him a few weeks before his death, he was bubbling with enthusiasm about a demonstration structure at the Centre for Alternative Technology at Machynlleth in Wales, and about a building his stepson was putting up on his smallholding, with three big frames, erected, like an American barn-raising, by emptying the local pub one weekend lunchtime.

His friends and the people who had changed their lives by building Walter's way, set up a Walter Segal Self-Build Trust to propagate the message and slowly, all around Britain, examples of his approach to house-building could be found. They are among the few bright lights in the dismal housing cli-

Low-energy Segal method house built at the Centre for Alternative Technology in Wales, by students on a self-build course there

mate of the 1990s. Just as he hoped, his successors have continually adapted his approach to meet their own needs, and to changing assessments of environmentally-friendly materials and standards of construction.

Readers who want to know more should seek out from their local public library The Self-Build Book (reviewed in the following pages) by Jon Broome and Brian Richardson, two architects and self-builders who worked closely with Segal. It was published by Green Books in 1991, sold out, and a new revised edition is expected in 1995. The book is about bringing the joy back into building.

Colin Ward is an anarchist writer. Many of his books are about popular and unofficial environments. Anarchy in Action; Talking Houses; Talking Schools; Freedom to Go; The Child in the City; The Child in the Country; and Welcome, Thinner City are all available from Freedom Bookshop, 84b Whitechapel High Street, London E1 7QX. His book Influences: Voices of Creative Dissent is published by Green Books, Foxhole, Dartington, Totnes, Devon TQ9 6EB

- The Walter Segal Self-Build Trust, 57 Chalton Street, London NW1 1MU. The Trust issues information and a bulletin on a shoestring, so please enclose an sae.

Chris Coates reviews: four books on self-building

I have to confess to having inherited from my father the trait of - if you want to know how to do something get a book about it, or even better get five books about it ! Which is how I come to possess copies of all the following books and have over the last few years become a veritable armchair self-builder. The cliche is that "everyone dreams of building their own home" and increasing numbers of people in this country are turning to self-build to answer their housing needs. Self - builders will soon be building more new houses per year than any single property developer.

Which probably goes a long way to explaining why there are so many good self-build books around at the moment. Why two of them are pro-duced by communities listed in D&D is another question.

Pat Borer & Cindy Harris *Out of the Woods* Centre for Alternative Technology Publications, ISBN 1 898049 12 2

This is a joint publication between the Walter Segal Trust and the Centre for Alternative Technology (CAT). After reading this book you could actually go out and build your own house. It is the culmination of the work that CAT have been doing to develop the Segal method of building (see previous article). It takes you through all stages of the self-build process and has a comprehensive breakdown of the ecological impact of every material that you might use in construction plus useful info on where to get enviromentally friendly building materials. Being a carpenter by trade I am biased towards this method of building and my only gripe about this book is that the cover did not last one day on site.

John L Talbot *Simply Build Green: A tech-nical guide to the ecological houses at the Findhorn Foundation* Findhorn Foundation, ISBN 0 905249 86 0

This is the technical story of the ecological village project at the Findhorn Community. It is a very good guide to the state of enviromental awareness in building techniques. Covering the enviromental impact of all aspects of building from different construction techniques through basic materials, energy use/conservation to fixtures/ fittings and shared facilities. The format is a sturdy loose leaf folder which would stand up well to being on a building site, however it is more a book for the planning stage of building than a hands-on how to do it guide. In fact I have never taken this book on site but refer to it regularly when plan-ning a building with groups.

John Broome & Brian Richardson *The Self-Build Book: How to enjoy Designing and Building your own Home* Green Books, ISBN 1 870098 23 4

Recently reprinted and updated this is the best general introduction to self-build (again Segal method) around. Both authors worked with Walter Segal on the early projects and have been involved with the ongoing devel-opment of the method. The first half of the book is made up of reports on vari-ous self-build schemes in Britain and Europe, which I found both inspiring and very useful on a practical organisational what to do/not to do level. The rest of the book is a good how-to-do-it guide. This was the first self-build book I bought and is the one that caught my imagination and inspired me to become involved in self-build. And before the CAT book came out was the one that got dirty on site.

Christopher Day *Building with Heart*
Green Books, ISBN 1 870098 08 0

Building with Heart is one architect's personal journey through self-build. Part practical journey, part almost spiritual journey. It covers various projects that the author worked on, mainly community buildings rather than housing, and gives an insight into a Rudolph Steiner inspired approach to building. Building is so much seen as rational/ logical and technical I found it liberating to come across an organic approach to building that stressed the spiritual/ inspirational/ aesthetic side of building. This book is also very good on the organisation of volunteers and site management for community projects.

Robert Matthews *Talking Self-build*
Blackberry Books, ISBN 0 9515295 0 1

These are the words of self-builders themselves: the highs, the lows, the practicalities and the satisfaction. A whole cross section of people interviewed by the author give you the lowdown on what building your own house really means. This was the book that convinced me that I could build my own house - that anyone could build their own house.

	Practicality	Inspiration	Eco-build advice
Out of the Woods	▰▰▰▰	✿✿	♣♣♣
Simply Build Green	▰	✿✿	♣♣♣
The Self-Build Book	▰▰▰	✿✿	♣♣
Building with Heart	▰	✿✿✿	♣
Talking about Self-Build		✿✿✿✿✿	

❂ A good source of books and videos on building, extending or renovating a home is Blackberry Books, 10 Bartholomew Street, Leicester LE2 1FA.

Chris Coates works as a site supervisor for community self-build projects and has recently won the North West Area Health Authority - Health Challenge Award for Greenspace Horticultural Therapy Project's new facilities - a building built by people suffering from mental illness.

How to do it

Are you just a commune groupie who visits communities but never moves in? Or worse, do you buy D&D every two years and just read about them? Whatever your diagnosis, this section is intended to help you cure your ailment and take a leap forward from "utopian dreaming to communal reality".

Could I live communally?

First get clear about your motivations:

• if you're trying to escape from the 20th/21st Centuries then forget it - pollution rains down on communes as well. Communities <u>may</u> be a better place from which to change society but beware: they suck up a lot of energy themselves.

• if you're trying to escape from responsibilities then forget it. The responsibilities of being a community member are usually far more onerous. OK, they're shared but that in itself has a personal energy "overhead".

• if you see it as an easy way of making friends, forget it. If you have difficulty making friends in the wider world it won't be any easier in a community.

• if you see it as a way of having more control over your own life then think hard about what you mean by this. In your present situation you probably think that most of the decisions about your life are made by distant bureaucracies. It's true that in a community more decisions will be made closer to you by people you know. You will participate in the decision-making but that doesn't mean that everything will go the way <u>you</u> want it to. There will be many areas where you quite happily make decisions yourself now (eg keeping a pet, what time you eat supper) which, in a community, you've got to agree with loads of other people.

• If you want all the joys of communality (and there are many) then cast aside your rose-tinted spectacles! We've put together this warts and all guide because we believe that communities will develop better if people arrive with realistic notions of how it will be when they get there.

General Point

Communal living won't solve all your problems. You have to be willing to look at yourself and your "psychological baggage" at every stage. Communards are usually very tolerant of different viewpoints but not of dramatists. Communal living is guaranteed to come up with events that will "press all your buttons". If you have a tendency to descend into drama then ask yourself why. Perhaps there is something from your past which you haven't dealt with? Fellow communards will usually be very supportive of people who are interested in changing and growing but the "stuck and apparently happy with it" person is a difficult one to deal with. All too often the clear waters of the communal pool are muddied by people's undealt with "stuff". This so easily leads to, what has been called, "emotional plague".

What should my next steps be?

- Think carefully about what exactly you're looking for.
- Consult the index on pp 110-111. If you don't have any capital then you can cut out all the places that require it. Now think about whether you want to share income (it always sounds attractive but what about your Mars bar addiction?). Not all communities eat communally but to those that do it will usually be quite a sacrosanct feature and opting out may be discouraged/ disallowed. If you consume a special diet then will the right food be available? We've asked communities that are either exclusively lacto-ovo-vegetarian or vegan to indicate this. If you're vegan decide whether you could cope with meat being cooked and eaten alongside you in a mixed diet community? You can also tell from the Index which communities are spiritually orientated.
- You should leave the Index with a shortlist of likely communities. Now refer to their entries in the main Directory - this will give you a better idea of what they're about. You may well have your own criteria (geographical location etc) to introduce so that by the end of this exercise you're left with a handful of places to write to and ask to visit.
- We would suggest that you don't join the first place that you come across without seeing what else is available.

What if a community I like is full?

We can't give you a definite answer on this one as attitudes will vary. Hosting visitors can be tiring and energy consuming and consequently some communities put up the barricades when they're full because there seems no immediate need to find new members. Others will continue to host visitors in the hope of building up a pool of people who know what their place is like and "might move in some day". In an ideal world perhaps all would do the latter but you shouldn't pressurise a place that doesn't offer this service.

If you bought D&D 96/97 by mail order then you should have received a sheet entitled **Places needing People** listing the communities currently seeking members. If you bought D&D in a bookshop then you can obtain the latest Places needing People by sending a 2nd class stamp to our distributors: Edge of Time Ltd (address on p 2).

General Point

Never make assumptions This is a good general rule for life but is crucial when visiting communities. Never has a type of organisation been so stereotyped by the media and consequently so many assumptions generated. If you're keen on naturism: don't assume that's it's ok to take your clothes off anywhere. It may well be but check first. If you're a dog-lover: don't assume that you can allow your beast to run wild (or even bring it with you in the first place!). Many of the points that follow will question your assumptions.

> AND DO YOU HAVE FREE LOVE HERE?

> IT COSTS AS MUCH AS IT DOES ANYWHERE ELSE

Can you give me any advice on visiting?

Visitors are important for most communities. They're needed for fresh ideas, interest and energy, plus of course valuable help with the work. Visitors are also where new members come from, an important consideration for most communities.

• Different communities have different approaches towards welcoming new people. Some places will have visitor weekends, when they concentrate their energies on a group of visitors. They discourage new visitors at other times because a continuous flow of new faces sometimes makes their home feel more like a hostel. Other places will have visitors almost all the time, but they usually try to make sure that there are no more than a couple of new people at any one time so that they don't feel swamped. Communities where people own their own units; have outside jobs during the day; and generally indulge in limited communal activity may find it difficult to welcome visitors on an ongoing basis.

• All communities prefer you to arrange a visit and not just to turn up. The important thing to remember is that a community is home for its members, and it can feel less than comfortable to have your home filled with uninvited guests. Write briefly, explaining who you are and what you're looking for. It may be that a particular community can tell straightaway that it's not the place for you, but if that's not the case, they'll usually reply with more detailed information. If, after reading it, you still want to visit then you can arrange a time. The length of stay permitted for a first visit will vary from place to place.

So what can you expect when - having packed your sleeping-bag, wellies, working clothes and hot water bottle - you find yourself at the door of your chosen community? We can't tell you because not only do communities vary enormously, but you could come upon each one in a different state or mood.

• You could arrive on a weekend when they're all collecting fire wood, or it's someone's birthday, or on a non-special occasion when there's a good group feeling. But it's as likely that you'll come upon them when they've just had a difficult meeting, or at a time when too many of them are away or ill, or have got things of their own that they want to get on with. They could be desperate for visitors after a dearth, or they could be desperate for some time and space to themselves after having had more new people here than they really wanted.

• An open mind is definitely an asset, and remember that however you find a community on your first visit, it isn't always like that. Generally however you can expect a nice cup of tea (or whatever you drink) and a tour around the place. You can expect to be asked to join in with whatever's going on, but you can always decline and ask if there's something more suited to your abilities and interests. One thing you can certainly expect is that help with the washing-up will be appreciated!

• Most communities make an effort to help people feel at home but, partly because they have visitors nearly all the time, they sometimes don't put in as much effort as they'd like. Say something if you feel neglected, either socially or for lack of things to do. If you feel shy or nervous, remember every member was a visitor once and they can probably remember what it was like.

• Some visitors do seem to forget that they're in someone's home, and it's not pleasant to have your home treated like an institution. Communities are not, generally, frightened of being criticised or challenged, but there is a limit and it helps if first there is some attempt to understand not only how things are but also why.

• Once you've got through your first visit you'll probably have a better idea of what you're looking for. If you want to visit again, they'll usually want to discuss this amongst themselves. If a community doesn't want you to return it could be for any number of reasons - try not to take it too personally and keep on looking for one where you will fit in.

What will I find?

Victoria Vassie recently completed a thesis (for her Environmental Studies degree at the University of Hertfordshire) about the function and activities of organisations presenting alternatives to the industrial system. The answers to her questionnaires give a good summary of intentional community characteristics and thinking for the uninitiated:

○ sizes vary between 10 and 30 with emphasis on the nuclear family reduced

○ organisational characteristics are considered to be a demonstration of an alternative

○ frequent contact with mainstream society is valued

○ distinctions between work/ community life and income generating/ domestic work are blurred

○ communal living as an end in itself is the most frequent reason given for the establishment of communities

○ means of income generation is diverse but usually human scale

○ structural and functional charactersitics: equality in decision making and distribution of work; non-hierarchical systems; democratic organisation; frequent worker ownership

○ frequent use of low-impact technology

○ diverse modes of transport

○ dominant concept of sustainability focuses on reduced consumerism and protection of eco-systems; practices follow accordingly

○ organisational strategy is designed to relate to ecological ideology; consistency in this is important

○ satisfaction of individual and social needs take priority over fulfilment of environmental needs

○ co-operation is quoted as the aspect of community life which most enhances quality of life

○ the majority of members are satisfied and would recommend communal life to others

Victoria concludes by noting that "Aspects of the framework of contemporary society inhibit the practice of ecologically orientated lifestyles. This represents the difficulties in establishing alternatives to contemporary industrial society whilst it is the prevailing regime. These factors should be considere when interpreting the work of communes and co-ops in order to avoid a purist analysis ... the communal environment is rarely a model of utopia contrary to some expectations of the inexperienced."

What should I be looking out for?

◦ Ask what the structure is that you would be joining. Many communities are also housing co-ops (in legal terms they are usually Industrial & Provident Societies - a particular kind of corporate body where the liability of members is limited to the value of their £1 share). Be aware of responsibilities that you might have as a member or director.

◦ Ask to see the "external rules" (usually a Constitution or a Memorandum & Articles of Association). Ask what happens in the event of dissolution of the community?

◦ Are there any "internal rules" - ask how are they enforced?

◦ What are the financial structures of the community? How does money come in and where does it all go? Ask to see the most recent audited accounts. Are there cash flow projections? Are any large sums owing to anyone and when are the repayments due? If you're expected to invest yourself you may be wise to take independent legal advice but beware, most solicitors are very unfamiliar with these kinds of legal structures so don't assume the worst just because your solicitor does (see addresses p109).

What are some of the worst things that can go wrong?

◦ It's rare for things to get this bad but take a story like this one (from Simon McEwan of Beech Hill) as a salutary warning:

"How do you feel if the fate of your long-established community hinges on a few tense minutes at a property auction? Answer: You feel very very nervous. Beech Hill Community was founded in 1983 at a spacious house in the heart of the mid Devon hills. The 20-room building dates back to the 18th century. Several outbuildings have been converted into five more homes and there are seven acres of grounds. The focus of the community has been primarily ecological, and there has been an emphasis on flexibility, with some residents working outside and others in the community. The original legal structure was a housing co-op, and financial problems stemmed from an agreement at the outset that loan stock would be tied to the value of the property. By the time some of the early members left, property values had shot up in the 80s boom and they were paid back correspondingly larger amounts.

In an attempt to stay solvent, the co-op split the property up into units, obtaining mortgages for some and selling others leasehold to existing or potential co-op members. There was income from rents and from course groups but by the early 90s high interest rates and questionable financial management drove the co-op into deeper and deeper trouble. In August 1993 it declared itself insolvent and liquidators were called in. Many members lost money - some their life savings. Most members clung on, staying in privately owned units and caravans as other parts of the house were locked up by the bailiffs. The liquidators seized much of the furniture and equipment, including the co-op's beloved old tractor. The freehold of the site, the grounds, lounge and kitchen became the property of a bank which had a charge on it, but no attempt was made to close these communal rooms.

For many months the future of the community was on a knife-edge. Insecurity and anxiety were ever-present. Renewal was made possible by one particularly generous new resident who loaned funds to buy back areas owned by the bank and two flats repossessed by building societies. The communal nature of Beech Hill was a bonus at this point, making the property unattractive on the open market. A stream of bemused potential buyers came to view the flats, but decided a 'commune' was not for them. Perhaps it was the tipi on the lawn or the sound of drumming which put them off.

Meanwhile, a new legal structure was set up, with a trust to own the property and a community co-operative to manage it. The freehold, grounds, kitchen and lounge were bought back for just £9,000 and two flats for just £14,000 each at the auction. The flats were among dozens of repossessed property auctioned in the conference room of a Plymouth hotel. In the crowd of about 100 buyers the communards rubbed shoulders uneasily with slick property speculators in natty suits who had hushed conversations into mobile phones. One communard was so stressed out she can recall crouching in a foetal position against the wall as the smooth-talking auctioneer delivered his patter and took bids from around the room. When the gavel fell to Beech Hill Trust for both flats there were astonished looks as communards hugged each other in unrestrained joy.

In March 1995 the third and last flat was bought back at a similar auction in the same hotel some months later - this time with generous financial help from individuals and several other communities which gave loans or gifts ranging from £20 to £1,000.

Now we are going from strength to strength. It has been a traumatic and long drawn-out struggle for survival but we feel that we have been bonded by what we have been through. A core group has held together through thick and thin, and we have some great new people. There is lots of energy and excitement about the future."

Is there a vision for the community?

It's tempting to join somewhere because you like the people and they like you. That's fine but remember that it's unlikely that that particular group of people will always be there. Times change and people move on and you may be better to choose according to the "spirit" of the community. Although the spirit is clearly created by the members it's uncanny how it often seems to exist independently of particular individuals.

° The premises which most communities occupy usually have huge potential but this "p-word" may well be banned in internal conversation. The reason is that it's often very difficult to bring together all the components (time, energy, money etc) which lead to fulfilment of potential in a group which is run by consensus and when a lot of the members are only there because they "just want to live communally". So if it's, say, building or business development that inspires you; then check out the priority that other members give to these areas.

° The same would apply to personal development - you can't assume that just because it's a community everything will just magically happen.

What do people eat?

° The popular image of communards as exclusively vegetarian is another media myth. In fact exclusively vegetarian communes are a rarity but, this said, you will probably find that the majority of meals served will be lacto-ovo-vegetarian (they may include eggs and/or dairy produce) and there will usually be a vegetarian alternative when there is meat.

° Veganism (other than in communities dedicated to it) is rather rarer. You may well find that smallholding based communes with house cows find veganism particularly difficult to cope with as so much of their diet will be dairy based.

° Always remember that cooking for large numbers is quite a big deal anyway and the complications multiply when a number of different diets have to be catered for. If your diet is fairly unusual and you're visiting then be prepared to bring food with you. If you're contemplating joining then talk with other members about the implications of your dietary needs; whether you may have to self-cater; and if so how acceptable this will be to others.

What happens after I've visited?

° The process will vary from place to place so check it out.

° Some communities will offer a probationary period (perhaps 3 or 6 months) after a few short visits. Others will require you to make more and longer visits but (if and when they decide positively) will give full membership straight away. There are good and bad sides to both systems and you're probably best to just accept whichever regime is in force.

° You have every right to demand clarity but try to be understanding of any difficulties that a group may have in coming to a decision about you. Your impression, as an outsider, may well be of a unified "them" against you. The reality is much more likely to be that there is a spread of views within the group; and the thing that takes the time is the group trying to come to a consensus. When you become a member yourself you will appreciate what they went through!

° If some members are unsure about you it will probably not enhance their opinion of you to be put under pressure. It's all much more complicated than going for a job interview - these people are going to have to share their lives with you and you with them. So allow time for the process.

What should be my concerns if I have children?

With the rural communities that have large estates people always say "It must be wonderful for kids to grow up here!" and that's usually true. But don't assume that your kids will always love it ...

• In these days of endless tabloid scare stories about child abductions it's great to know that there are places where kids can free-range in safety. But if you're keen on supervision remember that there's a price to pay: when you can't find them you may have 40 acres to search instead of your postage stamp sized garden in suburbia!

• How do you feel about other adults disciplining your kids? You'll need to be clear on this issue from the start.

• Kids usually love communal existence because there's an instant bunch of friends to play with. Within a relatively small group, however, age and gender imbalances may be a problem. If your joining of a group would further worsen an existing imbalance amongst the kids (or indeed the adults) then don't take it personally and try to recognise that were you to move in the situation might not be as attractive as you had perceived while you were a visitor.

• This applies to ratios of children to adults as well of course. Communities are undoubtedly good environments for single-parent families but a community made up exclusively of such groupings is likely to have a very high ratio of children to adults ... and this can be a nightmare ... for the single parents! So if you're a single parent and a community turns you down for this reason look at it as protecting you from a situation worse than the one that you're in at the moment.

• If you're just looking for someone else to take your kids off your hands then think again. Finding instant babysitters for sleeping children is pretty easy in a community but don't assume that instant free childcare is available 24 hours a day. Shared childcare happens all the time but there may be negotiating to do with other adults and, naturally, an expectation that you'll play your part. As a visitor, don't assume that you can just wave goodbye to your child when you arrive and pick them up again when you leave. They probably will disappear off with the other kids but try to keep track of them and, most importantly, make sure that they know where you are.

• More organised systems of shared childcare have been tried (eg a children's house with adult(s) rotating the role of carer) but these have usually been fairly short-lived. They've also often led to acute disappointment for non-parents when long nurtured relationships with children have been abruptly terminated when their parents have decided to move on.

• Quite a lot of what has been said already has applied to young children. With teenagers it's a different ball game altogether. Responses of adolescents vary a lot. The need to react against older generations invariably comes into play and the community becomes the ideal scapegoat. Peer group pressure is at its height in the teenage years and many commune adolescents find their residence, well ... frankly, embarrassing. One plus side for teenagers is usually the range of other adults that there are around - an ideal source of non-parental confidantes and mentors. You'll often find that a community has either loads of teenagers or none. This is one of the cases where the "like attracts like" phenomenon operates most clearly.

• Some communities do not welcome children at all and you should be sensitive to this.

• Most importantly ... ask your kids what they would feel about moving to a community and listen to what they say.

... and deschooling Communities are good places for home education because there are so many educative activities and people around. But don't rely on sharing the work with other home educating adults ... they may well have completely different ideas from you about learning methods. Another factor that you may well like to consider is that your kids will be living a very different life from their peers anyway. Do you want to make it 100% different by denying them access to school and wider contact as well?

● A good way of visiting communities is to join WWOOF - it's a way of helping people who run organic farms and smallholdings. Many communities are also WWOOF hosts.

WWOOF 19 Bradford Road, Lewes, East Sussex BN7 1RB

Do I have to become a clone?

People often ask how much compulsion there will be to conform. Will they <u>have</u> to get into African drumming; co-counselling; permaculture; or goat husbandry? Will they <u>have</u> to wear flared trousers ... or worse still - will they have to take them off and sit around naked in a sauna with other people?

● As usual it's going to vary from place to place. Communities associated with larger organisations may well have more elements of a "house style" that members are expected to conform with. This is part of the trade-off for the greater security which comes as a result of being part of something bigger. The consensus driven communities will usually value co-operation above conformity. However ...

● If some ritual (eg silent attunement before meetings, daily communal meals) is viewed as a very important part of communal life then you shouldn't consider joining if you have no intention of participating.

● There will always be a tension between individual freedom and the group spirit. If you want <u>total</u> individual freedom then a community is unlikely to be the place for you. If you see being part of a community as a way of achieving something greater than you can achieve by yourself then you'll recognise that there is a need to align people's dreams, visions and commitment. Shared belief systems; habits and activities which bring people together; are amongst the techniques which make this possible.

● But of course you can take this too far. A totally enclosed group whose life revolves around ritual can be very close but totally moribund in terms of wider achievement.

What if I'm ill/ disabled/ old?

● The communities that have been around for a longer time have more experience of dealing with these issues. Communities set up since the 60s often struggle with them because of an underlying ethos that every member contributes equally. Fine when all members are young, fit and able-bodied but an enormous guilt-trip to lay on the less able-bodied.

● The nub of it is that many communities live on the breadline. There is often little spare financial or personal energy capacity. Buildings can be cold in the winter and people have to give time to maintenance etc, rather than money that they don't have. For this

reason it can be difficult to imagine how an adult that needed a lot of care could come <u>into</u> a community without a carer and money (private or state) with which to pay them.

● Where baby-boomers who set up communes grow old still living in them, then systems will undoubtedly evolve to cope with this issue. Until then progress will be slow.

● There are exceptions and obviously some communities (eg Camphill and l'Arche) have a caring role as their focus. However this usually relates to people with special needs.

● Age, in itself, is not important but those who are young at heart will always be more welcome than those who are not.

What are the "work" issues?

There are as many different approaches to work as there are communities - just take a look at the Directory.

• The uninitiated usually assume that every one in a community works for the community and nobody else. In fact this is very rarely the case. There <u>are</u> income-sharing groups where the community runs a business in which every member is expected to work. The business produces the income which the group then shares. It sounds great and when the ideal works it can be very good. When it doesn't it can be worse than work in the outside world. If you fancy this workstyle then ask yourself whether you are happy to live, work and play with the same people. You'll be getting rid of the compartmentalisation of your life but also the possibilities for respite. If things are not going well in your 9to5 job then at least you can go home and moan about it to someone who has no connection with it. Not so in an income-sharing commune ... you'll find the same people sitting round the kitchen table when you get "home".

• Other potential problem areas are with the day-to-day running. Everyone (including all new members) must be committed to the business. However, there is often a reluctance - for whatever reason - to take on the more "businesslike" aspects (eg marketing and finance) and the neglect of these can affect the whole operation.

• With people joining and leaving the community all the time there can be a problem with continuity in the business. The communities that run trading operations for an associated charity often do better on this score because external trustees provide better continuity. But then, of course, there is a danger that they will be perceived as "the bosses" by ill-informed members.

• More commonly found within UK communities is a hotch-potch of businesses run by sub-sets of the membership and/or sometimes non-members. These will have legal structures separate from any that exist for housing members. People may be self-employed or employees of a worker co-op; an ordinary share company; or another self-employed person.

• If a business is using some part of the community's premises it's quite important to have a legal agreement between the parties. The "just-let-it-happen" approach is all very well until there's a disagreement and then all parties start quoting their version of the "agreement" that was never made. A classic lead up to this is resentment from a member who perceives a non-member benefiting.

• With a smallish group and different legal structures around it's highly likely that people will end up having to "wear more than one hat". This can make meetings very confusing!

• A community can seem the ideal setting for self-employment given that a major problem for self-employed people who work by themselves is isolation. On the whole it <u>is</u> a good combination but it's important to maintain boundaries. A self-employed person who has lots of diy skills, for instance, may find themselves continually called upon to deal with urgent maintenance problems. Other members may not realise how detrimental this can be to their self-employment.

• The positive aspects of working on site are clear to see: not having to travel to work; having flexibility about working hours; and of course a greater freedom from the feeling of exploitation. But if you have decided that, for you, the cons outweigh the pros then maybe an outside job wouldn't be so bad after all ...

• Acceptability of outside work varies according to the type of community. In the more private, unit-owning communities it will often be the norm for people to pursue careers and even 9to5 jobs. In other types it can prove quite a strain. It can make people question why they are living communally at all. On the other hand it <u>does</u> show people in the wider world that communards are just like other people and that communal living is a credible option for anyone.

... and state benefits

In communities that are legally housing co-ops the members are tenants and consequently are able to apply for and, if eligible, receive Housing Benefit. This will not necessarily be the case in other types of community. You may also be eligible for Income Support or Family Credit but membership of an income-sharing community is likely to affect these benefits.

"We visit and join communes because, naively or not, we are drawn towards a paradisiacal vision of life as we hope or want it to be" Graham Carey

How long can I expect to stay?

⊕ People often imagine that they will join a community for life. It does happen but it's rare. The surrounding culture is a culture of change and it's inevitable that this ethos seeps through into the world of communities and makes people feel restless. Research by David Pepper (of Oxford Brookes University) showed that there was a peak of people leaving after two years and again after ten years. Probably the best advice we can give is that you should act as if you're there for life even if you might leave tomorrow.

⊕ Communities are just a particular kind of organisation and like other organisations they may well retain people longer if they are prepared to give sabbaticals and opportunities for personal (and possibly career) development.

⊕ Communities that provide a decent living for their members are likely to be more stable; as will those whose membership is made up of parents of teenage children. A share in the equity value of the property is often a big incentive to stay ... but this may be politically unacceptable to some!

Is it easy to leave?

⊕ Most communities have a fairly continuous turnover and this will often mean that people you have grown to like leave. Then the place becomes a "different" community and you start all over again. This can be both stimulating and wearysome depending on your state of mind at the time.

⊕ It can often be difficult to discuss thoughts of leaving with other members. All too many leavers blame some event in the community as the trigger for their decision rather than just accepting that they've made a choice for themselves. The community as handy scapegoat yet again.

⊕ There is a real need for greater continuity in communes and better connections with ex-members would go a long way to making this happen. In the consensus-driven communities, however, input by non (current) members can often be seen as a threat. As a result potential support from ex-members is stifled.

⊕ A lot of people get "sorted out" in communities and then go on to achieve amazing things in the wider world. (One may ask why they couldn't achieve "amazing things" in the community ... but that's the way it has to be, perhaps!).

⊕ Many marketable skills come from communal living ... it's just a matter of presenting them correctly to employers!

ACCOUNTANTS
Janet Slade & Co Fourways House, 57 Hilton Street, Manchester M1 2EJ
✆ 0161 236 1493
Simon Erskine & Co
14a Downshire Hill, London NW3 1NR
✆ 0171 435 4484

SOLICITORS
Malcolm Lynch
Vassalli House, 20 Central Road, Leeds LS1 6DE
✆ 0113 242 9600
James Sinclair Taylor & Martin
9 Thorpe Close, Portobello Road, London W10 5XL
✆ 0181 969 3667

LEGAL STRUCTURE EXPERTS
Industrial Common Ownership Movement Vassalli House, 20 Central Road, Leeds LS1 6DE ✆ 0113 246 1737

	charge visitors?	location	number of adults	number of children	income sharing?	capital required?	daily communal meals?	dietary regime	spiritual focus	page no
The Abbey	☉	rural	6	0			☉	vtn	C	182
Centre for Alt Tech		rural	8	1			☉			160
Ashram	☉	urban	5	0			☉		C	150
Beech Hill	☉	rural	16	3						173
Beeston House	☉	urban	8	0			☉	vtn	C	146
Birchwood		rural	17	4			☉			152
Blackcurrent	☉	urban	9	0			☉	vtn		147
Bradwell Othona	☉	rural	250	150			☉		C	178
Brambles		urban	6	3	☉		☉	vgn		131
Braziers	☉	rural	13	2			☉			183
Brotherhood Church		rural					☉	vtn	C	133
Camphill Steiner Sch		urban	147	210	☉		☉		A	121
Canon Frome		rural	29	21		☉				153
Chicken Shack		rural	8							159
Christ the Sower	☉	rural	15	8					C	142
Columbanus	☉	urban	6	0			☉		C	168
Common Property		urban	6	2						217
Community Creation	☉	urban	8	0				vtn		193
Cornerstone		urban	15	1						132
Crabapple		rural	6	1	☉		☉			155
Darvell Bruderhof		rural	175	150	☉		☉		C	186
Earthworm	☉	rural	6	2			☉	vgn		154
Erraid Community	☉	rural	8	1			☉		S	117
Family Tree		urban	8				☉	vtn	C	190
Findhorn Foundation		rural	130	22			☉		S	119
Glaneirw		rural	3	3	☉		☉			162
Graigian Society		urban	4	0	☉		☉	vtn	S	194
The Grail	☉	urban	22	0	☉		☉		C	192
Grimstone	☉	rural	6	3	☉		☉		S	172
Gwerin		urban	18	3						151
Hengrave	☉	rural	23	0			☉		C	140
Iona	☉	rural	31	0			☉		C	118
Keveral Farm	☉	rural	14	3			☉			175
Laurels		urban	6	4						179
Laurieston Hall		rural	24	8						115

	charge visitors?	location	number of adults	number of children	income sharing?	capital required?	daily communal meals?	dietary regime	spiritual focus	page no
Lifespan	◕	rural	8	4			◕			129
Lothlorien	◕	rural	14				◕			116
Lower Shaw Farm	◕	urban	7	7						167
Mickleton Emmisary		rural	45	9			◕		S	164
Monimail Tower	◕	rural	11				◕	vtn		122
Monkton Wyld	◕	rural	16	3			◕	vtn		171
Mornington Grove	◕	urban	12	2			◕	vtn		189
The Neighbours		urban	9	4					C	148
NewBold House	◕	rural	25	0	◕	◕	◕	vtn	S	120
Old Hall	◕	rural	48	22	◕	◕				139
Paradise Community	◕	rural	45	8			◕	vgn	A	166
Parsonage Farm		rural	9	5			◕			138
Pennine Camphill		rural	55	20			◕		A	128
People in Common	◕	rural	7	3			◕			127
Pilsdon Community		rural	35	5	◕		◕		C	170
Plants for a Future		rural	15	5				vgn		174
Postlip Hall		rural	16	15		◕				165
Quaker Community	◕	rural	15	4				vtn	Q	145
Rainbow		urban	33	20						180
Redfield	◕	rural	15	12			◕			181
Salisbury Centre	◕	urban	6	0			◕	vtn	S	123
Scargill House	◕	rural	40				◕		C	134
Shrub Family	◕	rural	5	5						141
Simon Community		urban	45	0			◕			195
Sisters of the Church		urban	16	0	◕		◕		C	197
Somefriends	◕	urban	14	0			◕	vtn	Q	188
Space House		urban	6	0						130
St Francis	◕	rural	15	0	◕		◕	vtn	C	169
St Hugh's		rural	22	0					C	184
St Peter	◕	urban	4	0			◕		C	196
Talamh	◕	rural	10	1			◕			124
Taraloka	◕	rural	10	0			◕	vtn	B	156
Tipi Village		rural	80	50					S	161
Wild Lavender	◕	urban	6	0			◕	vtn		191

Are there any books that you'd recommend?

Yes, here's a selection divided into a number of categories. A ⊙ indicates that the book is still in print as far as we know. See also the books advertised on page 224.

ACADEMIC

ABRAMS, P and McCULLOCH, A (1976) *Communes, Sociology and Society* Cambridge University Press, Cambridge ⊙

BARKER, E (1989) *New Religious Movements: A Practical Introduction* HMSO, London ⊙

BERGER, B M (1981) *The Survival of a Counter-culture: Ideological Work and Everyday Life among Rural Communards* University of California Press, London ⊙

BIRCHALL, J (1988) *Building Communities the Co-operative Way* Routledge & Kegan Paul, London ⊙

KANTER, R M (1972) *Commitment and Community: Communes and Utopias in Sociological Perspective* Harvard University Press, Cambridge Massachusetts ⊙

KESTON, S K (1993) *Utopian Episodes: Daily Life in Experimental Colonies Dedicated to Changes in the World* Syracuse University Press ⊙

RIGBY, A (1974) *Alternative Realities: a study of communes and their members* Routledge & Kegan Paul, London.

BIOGRAPHICAL

KINKADE, K (1973) *A Walden Two Experiment: the first five years of Twin Oaks* MorrowNo

RIDDELL, C (1991) *The Findhorn Community - Creating a human identity for the 21st Century* Findhorn Press, Forres ⊙

FICTION

CALLENBACH, E (1978) *Ecotopia* Pluto Press, London ⊙

HUXLEY, A (1962) *Island* ⊙

Le GUIN, U K (1974) *The Dispossessed* New York ⊙

HISTORICAL

ARMYTAGE, W H G (1961) *Heavens Below: Utopian experiments in Britain 1560 - 1960* Routledge & Kegan Paul, LondonNo

HARDY, D (1979) *Alternative Communities in Nineteenth Century England* Longmans, London

MERCER, J (1984) *Communes: A Social History and Guide* Prism Press, Dorchester ⊙

MUMFORD, L (1959) *The Story of Utopias* Peter Smith ⊙

REXROTH, K (1975) *Communalism: from its origins to the Twentieth Century* Peter Owen, London. ⊙

PHILOSOPHY

McLAUGHLIN, C and DAVIDSON, G (1985) *Builders of the Dawn* Sirius, Mass ⊙

PEPPER, D (1991) *Communes and the Green Vision* Green Print, London ⊙

WARD, C (1985) *When We Build Again, Let's Have Housing That Works!* Pluto, London ⊙

PRACTICAL

ALEXANDER, C et al () *Pattern Language* ⊙

AUVINE, B et al (1981) *A Handbook for Consensus Decision-making: Building United Judgement* Center for Conflict Resolution, Madison, Wisconsin ⊙

BELL, G (1994) *The Pemaculture Garden* Thorsens ⊙

BELL, G (1992) *The Permaculture Way* Thorsens ⊙

BRADSHAW, J (1988) *Guide to House Buying, Selling and Conveyancing* Castle Books, Leamington Spa ⊙

BROOME J and RICHARDSON, B () *The Self-Build Book* Resurgence Books ⊙

COOVER, V; DEACON, E; ESSEN, C and MOORE, C (1981) *Resource Manual for a Living Revolution* New Society Publishers, Philadelphia ⊙

ENO, S and TREANOR, D (1982) *Collective Housing Handbook* Laurieston Hall Publications

JELFS, M (1982) *Manual for Action: Techniques to enable groups engaged in Action for Change* Action Resources Group ⊙

MacFARLANE, R (1986) *Financial Planning and Control: A Practical Guide* ICOM Co-publications, London. ⊙

RANDALL, R (1980) *Co-operative and Community Dynamics: Or your meetings don't have to be that bad!* Barefoot Books, London ⊙

TREANOR, D (1987) *Buying Your Home with Other People* NFHA and Shelter, London ⊙

Directory of Communities and Networks

The Directory is set out in regions. Groups that consider themselves to be more communal than not are allocated a page each and are listed in rough geographic sequence. Networks and embryonic communities are listed by region where appropriate, otherwise they are located in the section which begins on page 204. Many communal groups are (in legal terms) housing co-ops. However there are also many hundreds of other housing co-ops for which communality is not necessarily a focus. By popular demand we are providing, for the first time in D&D, listings of such housing co-ops. We do not pretend that this list is exhaustive but it *is* up-to-date at the time of publication. Many co-ops have restricted entry of some kind, those in the list preceded by a • have mentioned a restriction when responding to us. Please do not pressurise these or any other groups and always write first. *Never just turn up!!!*

Scotland

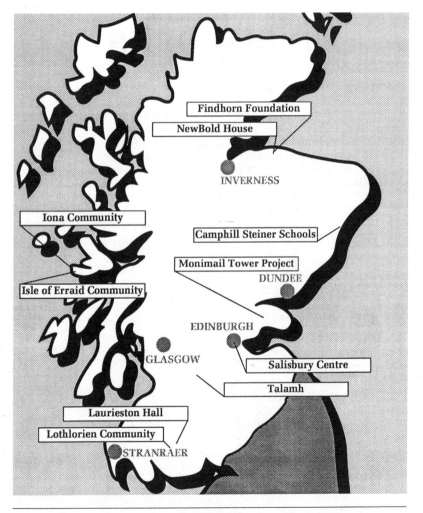

About half of us live in the main house, mostly in small groups sharing one of the three communal kitchens, and half live in cottages or caravans. Although each adult or family is domestically and financially independent, we work and play together. The day-to-day running of various work areas is largely done by people taking responsibility for what they see needs doing. The major areas - garden, wood, maintenance, dairy, finance, land - are managed by "committees" which meet regularly. Our "play" has included creating pantomimes and fire festivals. Some of us play cricket and bridge. There's a resident international folk dance band and various other groupings of people and instruments. We are not actively seeking new members. We tend to leave it to visitors who are interested in living here to make the first move, and they usually do this with encouragement from friends they make among residents. During our three Maintenance Weeks, when we function as one communal group, visitors are invited to join in with building maintenance, gardening, land work and domestic work. Another way of visiting is to come to a 'People Centre' holiday, event or workshop - please write for details.

LAURIESTON HALL

Status
existing community

Address
Laurieston
CASTLE DOUGLAS
Kirkcudbrightshire
DG7 2NB

Telephone

Number of over 18s
24

Number of under 18s
8

Year started
1972

Situation
rural

Ideological focus
no one word!

Legal structure
Co Ltd by Guarantee

Open to new members?
Yes

Photograph: Alice

LOTHLORIEN COMMUNITY

Lothlorien was established in 1978. It consists of a large log house with 14 bedrooms and communal living areas. It is set in seventeen acres of grounds which include organic vegetable gardens, woodland, workshops and outbuildings. In 1989, Rokpa Trust, which has grown out of Samye Ling Tibetan Buddhist Centre took over the running of Lothlorien. Its

Status
existing community

Address
Corsock
CASTLE DOUGLAS
Kirkcudbrightshire
DG7 3DR

Telephone
01644 440602

Number of over 18s
14

Number of under 18s

Year started
1978

Situation
rural

Ideological focus
various

Legal structure
Registered Charity

Open to new members?
Yes

aim is to maintain a supportive community in Lothlorien, where those who suffer from mental health problems can grow and develop through participation in community life. The guiding principles of the community are hospitality, care and respect for the person, and a belief that the potential of the individual can be encouraged through a communal life in which all have a contribution to make. There are places for four live-in volunteers who play a key role in helping to create a warm, accepting atmosphere in the community. Lothlorien now employs a manager, support worker and garden co-ordinator who provide a continuity of support to the community. We have vacancies on a regular basis as we see Lothlorien asa place where people can grow and develop for a period of time (usually up to one year). People are then encouraged to move on rather than seeing Lothlorien as their long term home. Please contact the manager by phone or letter if you have any queries.

The Erraid Community is a self-supporting part of the Findhorn Foundation. The thread bringing us together is our desire for a holistic quality of life and a greater expression of our divinity. Meditation is important, helping us to discover the right action for ourselves as individuals and for the Community as a whole. Erraid is an island on the south-western tip of Mull. Its square mile displays physical features typical of this part of Scotland where granite outcrops and peat bogs support an abundance of wild flowers. The climate can be extremely variable. We live in a five acre walled settlement with cottages, outbuildings and enclosed gardens. The resident group on Erraid numbers around ten: single people, couples and families (children thrive here). Our work is varied and balanced between individual focuses and working together. Meals are generally communal and mostly vegetarian, much of our food coming from our organic gardens, our dairy cows, poultry and the sea. Throughout most of the year we share our homes with guests, aware that our Community serves an educational purpose for all who come here. We welcome enquiries from people interested in participation in our life and work.

ISLE OF ERRAID COMMUNITY

Status
existing community

Address
Isle of Erraid
Fionnphort
Isle of Mull
Argyll
PA66 6BN

Telephone
01681 700384

Number of over 18s
8

Number of under 18s
1

Year started
1978

Situation
rural

Ideological focus
spiritual

Legal structure
Registered Charity

Open to new members?
Yes

Drawing: Anne Whitbread

IONA COMMUNITY

The Iona Community, an ecumenical Christian community, invites volunteers over the age of 18 to come for six to eighteen weeks to share in a ministry of welcome and hospitality. Members of the community are scattered throughout the world. Volunteers are not members but come to the historic island of Iona to share alongside guests in a weekly programme of work, worship and recreation.

The food is mainly vegetarian (though all diets are catered for) and meal times are important times of contact with guests. Volunteers work as kitchen and housekeeping assistants; in the coffee shop, and Abbey Bookshop; and as craftworkers and guides. They receive £17 per week pocket money and return travel expenses within the UK. Accommodation is shared with two or three others. An age, gender and international balance is maintained.

Applications are received throughout the year and invitations for voluntary places are sent out in January for the season, which runs from March to November. Contact the Staff Co-ordinator for further information.

Status
existing community

Address
Isle of Iona
Argyll
PA76 6SN

Telephone

Fax
01681 700460

Number of over 18s
31

Number of under 18s
0

Year started
1938

Situation
rural

Ideological focus
Christian

Legal structure
Registered Charity

Open to new members?
not applicable

The Findhorn Foundation is an international spiritual community in north-east Scotland. It was founded in 1962 by Eileen and Peter Caddy and Dorothy Maclean on the principles that God, or the source of life, is accessible to each of us at all times, and that nature, including the planet, has intelligence and is part

FINDHORN FOUNDATION

of a much larger plan. While we have no formal doctrine or creed, we believe an evolutionary expansion of consciousness is taking place in the work, creating a human culture infused with spiritual values. The Foundation, a charitable trust, is a centre of education and demonstration. It began with three adults and three children in a barren corner of a caravan park and now includes approximately 150 resident members of varying ages and nationalities living in several sites in the area. A wider community or 'village' is growing here as people with shared values and vision are coming to live alongside the Foundation. We invite you to join us in the experience of our living education. Come and help us create a positive vision and future for humanity and the planet! Information about workshops, conferences and guest programmes are available from the Accommodation Secretary.

Status
existing community

Address
Cluny Hill College
FORRES
Morayshire
IV36 0RD

Telephone
01309 673655

Fax
01309 673113

Electronic Mail
vcentre@findhorn.org

World Wide Web
http://www.mcn.org/
findhorn/home.html

Number of over 18s
130

Number of under 18s
22

Year started
1962

Situation
urban & rural

Ideological focus
spiritual

Open to new members?
Yes

NEWBOLD HOUSE

In a rural setting a 100 year old Victorian house is home to an intentional community where we explore creative ways of living and working together in harmony with each other and our environment. Our purpose as a spiritual and educational centre is fulfilled in several ways: we run a variety of spiritual and personal growth workshops, short term guest programmes and long term guest programmes (three months).

We are part of the Findhorn Community but independent of the Findhorn Foundation and are committed to bring about the highest ideals of the Findhorn Foundation in our own unique way, becoming yet another expression of the same spirit.

We have a diverse approach to spirit in our membership. Our structures are quite formal and tend to follow the general pattern of the Findhorn Foundation. All our money dealings are done by attunement, eg no set allowances for members, each member attuning to their needs, each member attuning to the community in terms of an entrance fee. Decisions are made on a consensus basis only. There are two formal channels for dealing with relationships - family meetings and members' meetings. There is a general openness to exploring ways of keeping all relationships clear between all members.

We have a large garden but the emphasis in the garden is education rather than self sufficiency. Our diet is vegetarian. Work includes maintaining the grounds, gardens, education programs and the general running of a centre such as reception, cooking etc. We have six acres of land and each member has their own living space. We are very willing to respond to enquiries. All prospective members are required to participate in the three month guest program before considering membership.

Status
existing community

Address
St Leonards Road
FORRES
Morayshire
IV36 0RE

Telephone
01309 672659

Number of over 18s
25

Number of under 18s
0

Year started
1979

Situation
rural

Ideological focus
New Age

Legal structure
Registered Charity

Open to new members?
Yes

This community is a residential school for about 140 pupils "in need of special care". The children and co-workers, ie house-parents, teachers, nurses, etc, and the many helpers, share all aspects of life as part of extended families, living in about 18 houses of various sizes, spread over two different estates. The aim of the community is to help the children, who are referred by local authorities, to develop to their fullest potential. This aim is pursued with the help of the educational methods of the Waldorf School Movement, a medical, therapeutic and social approach inspired by Rudolf Steiner, the founder of Anthroposophy.

CAMPHILL RUDOLF STEINER SCHOOLS

Fundamental to this community is also that its members do not receive wages, but try to share the common resources in a brotherly way. We are always looking for co-workers, who are willing to share the intensive social life and able to take an active role in the life with the children. More than half of the co-workers are young people who come for a year from all over the world to gain new experiences. There is the possibility to join the three year course in Curative Education; we hope to inspire people to make Camphill their way of life.

Status
existing community

Address
Central Office
Murtle Estate
Bieldside
ABERDEEN
AB1 9EP

Telephone
01224 867935

Fax
01224 868420

Number of over 18s
147

Number of under 18s
210

Year started
1940

Situation
semi-urban

Ideological focus
Anthroposophy

Legal structure
Co Ltd by Guarantee

Open to new members?
Yes

MONIMAIL TOWER PROJECT

Monimail Tower is the only remains of Cardinal Beaton's Palace built in the 16th century. In 1985 a community was started on the land around the Tower. Most of the land is woodland. There is also a large orchard and walled garden. We now live in our first permanent building as well as some temporary huts.

Status
existing community

Address
Letham
by CUPAR
Fife
KY7 7RJ

Telephone
01337 810420

Number of over 18s

Number of under 18s

Year started
1985

Situation
rural

Legal structure
Registered Charity

Open to new members?
Yes

We try to share as much as possible from food and work to skills and resources. We eat a mostly vegetarian diet, organic if possible. The main areas of responsibility are the garden, the woods, building, maintenance and administration. We pay rent to the project and do not share incomes. We would like to find more ways to become self-supporting. We also like to meet people, play music, dance and generally have fun. We have meetings once a week and make our decisions by consensus. Our aim is to build a resource for ourselves and other people with which to learn how to live together in a way that is beneficial to all. We are open to people from whatever background to visit and take part. For more information please write enclosing a stamped addressed envelope.

The Salisbury Centre is a spiritual centre focusing on spiritual, physical and emotional healing. It was established in 1973 by Dr Winifred Rushforth, who was a leading Scottish psychotherapist and dream analysist. The Centre is a large Georgian house and organic garden, near Arthur's Seat and within walking distance of the City Centre. Six people live here communally in a self-contained flat. There is also two meditation rooms, studio, library, kitchen, pottery and office. Our life together operates on trust, openness and a mutual respect for our individuality and space. We are learning and growing continually and as residents generally stay between one and three years, the Centre flows and flourishes with change, but is rooted in history and hours of mediation and prayer. On Fridays we work in the house and garden together, meditate and share lunch; anyone is welcome to come to this. We are open to visitors who would like to stay and experience community life. We draw a basic income from the co-op, our work is diverse with the upkeep of the house and garden and administration. Together we produce a programme three times a year, consisting of: meditation, yoga, belly dancing and drumming to psychic development, reflexology and didgereedoo workshops.

SALISBURY CENTRE

Status
existing community

Address
2 Salisbury Road
Newington
EDINBURGH
EH16 5AB

Telephone
0131 667 5438

Number of over 18s
6

Number of under 18s
0

Year started
1973

Situation
urban

Ideological focus
spiritual

Legal structure
Co Ltd by Guarantee

Open to new members?
Yes

TALAMH

Status
existing community

Address
Birkhill House
COALBURN
Lanarkshire
ML11 0NJ

Telephone
01555 820555

Number of over 18s
10

Number of under 18s
1

Year started
1993

Situation
rural

Ideological focus
ecological

Legal structure
Unincorporated

Open to new members?
Yes

Talamh (earth/soil) has grown to a group of ten residents and two long term volunteers since our last entry in D&D. We started in January 1993 and live in a 16th century farmhouse with 50 acres of land which is managed as a species habitat with fun/education space. We are eventually aiming for self-sufficiency and our main focus is the environment and people. Some members are actively involved with environmental organisations. We have started to run courses and are a venue for seminars, workshops and talking shops. We are hoping to continue to develop as a venue for education in energy efficiency, renewable methods of production, environmental education, holistic health and individual development by having an atmosphere where people can relax, take time for themselves and learn from or give to Talamh. We run a non-profit voluntary conservation organisation with a monthly programme of practical work promoting land management for wildlife on our own site and into our local community. We no longer income share and everyone pays a rent which copes with all communal necessities. At our weekly meetings decisions have thus far been achieved by consensus (although not everyone would agree with that). Any visitors are welcome (particularly if they want to help out). We cook vegetarian food but will cater for meat eaters and vegans.

HOUSING CO-OPS IN SCOTLAND

Ormiston People's Housing Co-operative
*The Square, Ormiston Crescent,
Dundee DD4 0UD. 220 Ad.*

Vale of Duntrune Community H.A.
*7 The Willows, Whitfield, Dundee
DD4 0ZB. 01382 502411. 170 Ad.*

Auchinleck Housing Society Ltd (Amazon Lodge)
*20 Stanley Road, Edinburgh.
0131 552 0071. 7 Ad.*

Ploughshare Housing Co-op
*16 Westhall Gardens, Bruntsfield,
Edinburgh EH10 4JQ.
0131 229 1051. 9 Ad.*

Bath Street Housing Co-operative
*9 Bath St, Portobello, Edinburgh
EH15 1EZ. 0131 669 3924.
7 Ad, 1 Ch.*

Lister Housing Co-operative
*36 Lauriston Place, Edinburgh,
EH3 9EZ.*

Cernach Housing Co-operative
*Unit 20/21, Ladylon Place, Glasgow
G15 8LB. 0141 944 3860. 230 Ad.*

Pineview Housing Co-operative
*3 Rozelle Avenue, Glasgow G15.
0141 944 3891. 200 Ad.*

Kendoon Housing Co-operative
*50 Kendoon Avenue, Drumchapel,
Glasgow G15. 0141 944 8282.
150 Ad, 30 Ch.*

Blochairn Housing Co-operative
*311 Roystonhill, Royston, Glasgow
G21 2HN. 0141 553 1601. 14 Ad.*

Calvay Co-operative
*55 Calvay Road, Barlanark,
Glasgow G33 4RQ.*

Hickbrook Tenant Management Co-op
*201 Hollybrook Street, Govanhill,
Glasgow G42 8SS. 0141 422 1029.
215 Ad.*

Rosehill Housing Co-operative
*250 Peat Road, Rosehill, Glasgow
G53 6SA. 0141 881 0595. 430 Ad.*

West Whitlawburn Housing Co-operative
*Belmont House, 57 Belmont Road,
Cambuslang, Glasgow G72 8PG.
0141 641 8628.*

Easthall Park Housing Co-operatives
*37 Eastwood Road, Eastham,
Easterhouse, Glasgow.
0141 771 7088.*

Ferguslie Park Housing Association
*The Tannahill Centre, 76
Blackstown Road, Ferguslie Park,
Paisley PA3 1NT.*

Fairfield Housing Co-operative
*5 Fairfield Avenue, Perth PH1 2TF.
01738 630738. 320 Ad, 700 Ch.*

North of England

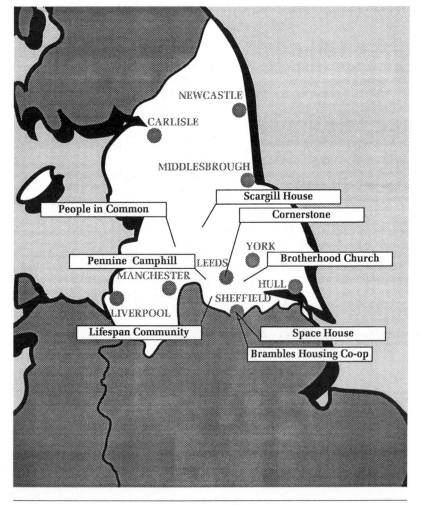

In the summer of 1988 we moved from the terraced houses in Burnley which were bought as a short-term stepping stone in the mid 1970s, to live in Altham Cornmill, the renovation of which is is nearing completion. The Mill is an historic early industrial building situated on Burnley's urban/rural fringe. There are about four acres of land, including riverbank, in which we are developing kitchen, ornamental and wildlife aspects as well as varied playspaces. All gardening is organic.

On site we have a cooperative business making oak beams and timber for the restoration of old buildings, which involves some of us. Other people's employment includes counselling, community development, single parenting, gardening, accountancy and teaching cookery to disabled people. Some of us live in separate units, while sharing some group facilities. There is a vegetarian communal group, which is hoping to expand. We have two cats, but don't want any more pets.

We have a strong commitment to cooperation, equality and the left, global and ecological perspectives, as well as being non-exploitative humourists. Our enthusiasms include cycling, playing bridge, circle dancing, art, radical politics, computors and roleplaying - and some of us still find time to read *The Guardian*.

There is a possibility of us being able to buy land nearby, which we hope to develop as a self-build housing co-op.

We are looking for people to join us to help develop the projects we are working on, especially a woman with skills to work in the timber business or set up a spin off to it. There is also a possibility for a horticultural project on the field.

If you are interested in visiting, please write to us with details about yourself.

PEOPLE IN COMMON

Status
existing community

Address
Altham Corn Mill
Burnley Road
Altham
ACCRINGTON
Lancashire
BB5 5UP

Telephone

Electronic Mail
pic@gn.apc.org

Number of over 18s
7

Number of under 18s
3-14

Year started
1973

Situation
semi rural

Ideological focus
eclectic

Legal structure
Ind & Prov Society

Open to new members?
Yes

PENNINE CAMPHILL COMMUNITY

Status
existing community

Address
Boyne Hill House
Chapelthorpe
WAKEFIELD
WF4 3JH

Telephone
01924 254054

Fax
01924 240257

Number of over 18s
55

Number of under 18s
20

Year started
1977

Situation
semi-rural

Ideological focus
Anthroposophy

Legal structure
Co Ltd by Guarantee

Open to new members?
Yes

We support a college for those with learning difficulties. Co-workers and their families live and work with 43 students. Our students have a range of abilities with mental, social, or emotional difficulties. Each of the four households is run on an extended family basis with shared mealtimes and common areas. Students live in the community during term time and attend classes or participate in the workshops and working life. The co-workers all work on a voluntary basis receiving no wage or salary but their daily needs are met by the community. There is always an international flavour to the community with usually half the co-workers coming from other countries. A small farm and vegetable gardens are worked biodynamically and provide much of the Community's needs. There are several craft workshops including a wood workshop, pottery, weaving and basket workshop, with facilities for other crafts. A college building houses classrooms, a bakery and a hall in which plays, folk dancing, and festive occasions are celebrated. We are always open to enquiries; our usual request is that a potential co-worker has a year free of commitments and would be prepared to live, work and learn alongside other in the community.

Lifespan consists of a group of people with differing ideals and attitudes to life who have only known each other for months, and have inherited nineteen dilapidated houses standing in dubious splendour amidst the Yorkshire moors. Our first aim is to learn how to live together, with acceptance, tolerance and respect, to like each other because of, rather than despite, our differences. We believe that only by having a diverse group capable of living and working in harmony can we create a sustainable, self-reliant alternative to the "nuclear" lifestyle. Our common bond is our sincerity in choosing to live as a community. In being able to see the far-reaching consequences of building a place where sharing and co-operation are key considerations. The pursuit of these ideals involves patience, understanding, ideas and vision, energy, enthusiasm and lots of hard work. Progress would not be possible without some structure, plans and people willing to take on big responsibilities. What do we actually do? We cook (for vegans and meat-eaters!), clean, build, garden, keep livestock and are building up income-earning businesses to eventually allow us not to claim state benefits. We also have time to paint, swim, walk dogs, play bad volleyball and party. We haven't always got our act together, (we are not perfect), but we are each of us doing what we can to help pave the way to a more sustainable, enjoyable future. There is much work ahead, this is just a small beginning, with no end project in sight yet. We intend to give it our best shot and if you have something to offer to our effort you will be made welcome. We need people with drive, commitment, dedication, green fingers, transport, home-educated kids, practical skills of almost every sort and above all a sense of humour. Be prepared to take us as you find us, in a good period life here is unbelievably sweet, on a bad day it can leave a very sour taste. If you can come along with an open mind, a willing body and a warm heart, write and tell us about yourself and what dates you'd like to visit.

LIFESPAN COMMUNITY

Status
existing community

Address
Townhead
Dunford Bridge
SHEFFIELD
S30 6TG

Telephone
01226 762359

Fax
01226 762359

Number of over 18s
11

Number of under 18s
4

Year started
1974

Situation
rural

Ideological focus
practical ecology

Legal structure
Ind & Prov Society

Open to new members?
Yes

SPACE HOUSE

Status
existing community

Address
8 Beaufort Road
SHEFFIELD
S10 2ST

Telephone
0114 267 0308

Number of over 18s
6

Number of under 18s
0

Year started
1994

Situation
urban

Ideological focus
non-doctrinal

Open to new members?
Yes

The Space House grew rapidly out of an idea developed by two people, to build community in the city. A large Victorian terraced house in a busy district of Sheffield was renovated to a high standard in the summer of 1994. Everyone involved in the work, professional builders and decorators and some of the residents, experienced some sense of community developing right from the start. The house opened in September 1994. We began working to build a communal way of life with a non-doctrinal approach based on quality and service. Interest has grown in the areas of personal growth, ecology, permaculture, charity and community work, counselling, ancient and modern teachings and meditation. The front room is now being used each morning for meditation by some of the residents and other early risers! It is also made available to certain other groups. A permaculture project with professional guidance is beginning around the house and gardens. We are planning to introduce a lending library in the house based in holistic approaches and teachings for life, and this will become part of what the house can offer to the wider community. Social activities organised by the household include rambles, cycle rides, pot luck meals and outings in the Peak National Park nearby. Facilities in the house are good and extensive with a separate space for each members. Tasks and upkeep of all communal areas are shared and a weekly house discussion meeting has become established. No financial commitment is required of members other than rent. Food costs are shared though meal arrangements are quite flexible. We eat together when our time-tables allow, as we all work out of the house at different times. We look forward to making contact and sharing experiences through Diggers and Dreamers.

Situated on a windy hill in Sheffield, Brambles Co-op and Resource Centre is home to six adults and three children. We have two houses and a large garden. The bottom of 82 acts as a Resource Centre: meeting room, office and library which is open for use by local groups. We are interested in promoting co-ops and co-operation within the inner city as well as providing a supportive community for ourselves and ways of living and working that are fun, empowering and sustainable. We are looking for people with enthusiasm and commitment to join us or set up similar projects in this area. For us co-operative living is an on-going experiment, learning new skills, the ups and downs of living with each other, being able to make mistakes and learn from them. We income share and members put in a full time commitment, sharing all work including childcare. The children here are de-schooled and we encourage them to be as involved as possible in the day to day life of the co-op. We aim to register a workers co-op in the near future. We are part of Radical Routes. Visitors are welcome but please ring or write first.

BRAMBLES HOUSING CO-OP

Status
existing community

Address
80-82 Andover Street
Burngreave
SHEFFIELD
S3 9EH

Telephone
0114 279 7164

Number of over 18s
6

Number of under 18s
3

Year started
1992

Situation
urban

Ideological focus
co-operation

Legal structure
Ind & Prov Society

Open to new members?
Yes

CORNERSTONE HOUSING CO-OP

Cornerstone is a small housing co-op set up in 1993 in order to provide a base for people involved in social and environmental issues. The co-op has recently bought its second house (up the road from the first) in the Chapeltown area of Leeds. Both are large, Victorian brick houses with gardens front and back. Our first house has a workshop used by Tools for Self Reliance and a resource centre and meeting room for the use of voluntary groups in the basement. In the second house we hope to develop a community arts space with studio/rehearsal rooms and a dark room.

The members of the co-op try to live communal, low-consumption lifestyles and are all vegetarians or vegans. United in at least eight different visions (so far) and being members of Radical Routes, the evening meal is often the setting for lively debate over the 1001 different ways to define "social change"! There is a roughly equal number of men and women aged from eight weeks to early forties, We have a dog called Sandy and a cat called Twyford.

Status
existing community

Address
16 Sholebroke Avenue
Chapeltown
LEEDS
LS7 3HB

Telephone

Number of over 18s
15

Number of under 18s
1

Year started
1993

Situation
urban

Ideological focus
social & environmental justice

Open to new members?

W e endeavour to follow the teaching of Christ's Sermon on the Mount. We are a land based community, and we aim at self sufficiency and acknowledge the supremacy of God rather than the rule of the state. We welcome visitors at all times. We conduct our own marriage ceremonies, funerals etc. Over the past two years we have had one wedding, one funeral and three memorial tree planting ceremonies, plus an annual Strawberry Tea Gathering (150-200 people).

BROTHERHOOD CHURCH

The Brotherhood Church came into being around 1898 and moved on to the land here in 1921 and has been totally organic ever since. We have a propaganda pulpit board by the roadside on which we like to keep a topical message. We are a totally pacifist group which is an affiliate of the War Resisters International. Our members feel that the peace witness is very important and do not shrink from the consequences of disobeying the laws of the state, if the state's laws are immoral. Not all members actually live at Stapleton. We have facilities for groups to meet - day, weekend or longer.

Status
existing community

Address
Stapleton
PONTEFRACT
Yorkshire
WF8 3DF

Telephone
01977 620381

Number of over 18s

Number of under 18s

Year started
1898

Situation
rural

Ideological focus
Christian

Open to new members?
Yes

BROTHERHOOD CHURCH

'SO LONG AS WE HAVE AN ECONOMIC SYSTEM THAT IS DESIGNED TO TAKE CARE OF THE SMALL GROUP WHO CONTROL THE WEALTH, THERE WILL BE HUNGER JOBLESSNESS & DISPAIR. WE MUST TAKE A NEW LOOK AT THE PROFIT SYSTEM, OR THERE IS SOMETHING BASICALLY WRONG.' (MARTIN LUTHER KING)

SCARGILL HOUSE

Status
existing community

Address
Kettlewell
SKIPTON
North Yorkshire
BD23 5HU

Telephone
01756 760234

Fax
01756 760499

Number of over 18s
40

Number of under 18s

Year started
1959

Situation
rural

Ideological focus
Christian

Legal structure
Co Ltd by Guarantee

Open to new members?
Yes

Scargill House is a holiday and conference centre in the Yorkshire Dales which opened in 1959 as a centre of evangelism and renewal for the churches in the North of England. Although it is an Anglican foundation the original vision included staffing the centre with a Community of Christians from all walks of life and Christian denominations. Community members are divided into six teams - Chaplaincy, House, Kitchen, Pantry, Estate and Office covering the various functions of running what is basically a conference centre but with the addition of Christian input. All Community members have an opportunity of leading worship and of ministering to the guests. The prime purpose of the Community is to serve the guests. Community members eat in the dining room with the guests. The majority of Community members are single, lay and young but the Chaplaincy team comprises priests, women deacons and lay readers. The overall policy of Scargill House is the responsibility of the Council who are prominent members of the Church, both lay and ordained. The buildings accommodate 90 guests and apart from several large lounges for conferences there is a fine Chapel, Library, Quiet Room and Games Room. Enquiries for private bookings should be made to the Bookings Secretary, for conference to the Conference Secretary and for Community membership to the Administrator.

HOUSING CO-OPS IN NORTH EAST ENGLAND

●**Railway Street Housing Co-operative**
19 Railway Street, Langley Park,
Durham DH7 9YS. 12 Ad, 8 Ch.
West End Housing Co-operative
2 Wellesley Terrace, Fenham,
Newcastle upon Tyne NE4 5NL.
0191 273 6418. 16 Ad, 7 Ch.
Summerhill Housing Co-operative
6 Summerhill Terrace, Newcastle
upon Tyne NE4 6EB.
0191 273 6418. 14 Ad.
Albion Housing Co-op
Albion Court, 100 Albion Row,
Byker, Newcastle upon Tyne
NE6 1LR. 12 Ad.
New Moves Housing Co-operative
27a Claremont Place, Claremont
Road, Newcastle upon Tyne.
Newhope Housing Co-operative
c/o Newcastle & Whitley, Milburn
House, Dean St, Newcastle upon Tyne.
Ath Gray Housing Co-op
Peel Street Housing Co-operative
●**Tatham Street Housing Co-operative**
all care of The Co-op Centre, 1a Salem

Street South, Hendon, Sunderland
SR2 8EY.
Riverside Housing Co-operative
4 Chilton Street, Southwick,
Sunderland SR5 1HN.
0191 549 2923. 160 Ad, 70 Ch.
Langridge Crescent Housing Co-operative
Initiative Centre, Langridge Crescent,
Middlesbrough, Cleveland TS3 7LU.
01642 240313. 147 Ad, 57 Ch.
Rothbury Road Tenant Management Co-op
28 Rothbury Road, Berwick Hills,
Middlesbrough, Cleveland
TS3 7NW. 01642 252166.
Oxfield Housing Co-operative Association
17 Oxfield, Coulby Nunham,
Middlesbrough, Cleveland.

SUPPORT ORGANISATION
Banks of the Wear Community Housing
Association
North Sands Business Centre,
Liberty Way, Sunderland SR6 0QA.
0191 514 2823.

HOUSING CO-OPS IN NORTH WEST ENGLAND

Burnleywood Housing Co-op
39 Kirkgate, BURNLEY, Lancashire
BB11 3NL. 01282 36932. 5 Ad, 5 Ch.
Eldonian Community Based Housing Ass
The Tony McGann Centre,
Burlington Street, Liverpool L3 6JG.
0151 207 3406.
Westvale Housing Co-operative *23 Manor*
Grove, Westvale, Kirkby, Liverpool
L32 0UZ. 0151 546 4640. 65 Ad, 74 Ch.
Westhead Housing Co-operative
c/o Kirkby Unemployed Centre,

Westhead Avenue, Northwood,
Kirkby L33 0XN.
Princes Park Housing Co-operative
c/o 1/5 Walton Road, Liverpool
L4 4AD. 0151 706 6300.
Vauxhall Housing Co-operative (Liverpool)
84 Boundary Street, Liverpool
L5 9RW. 0151 298 1544. 482 Ad.
Queens Court Housing Co-operative
21 Mackenzie Close, Liverpool L6
2LL. 0151 263 7580. 35 Ad, 25 Ch.

DIGGERS AND DREAMERS 96/97

Demeter Collective Housing Co-op
39 Kelvin Grove, Liverpool L8 3UE.
0151 727 4608. 5 Ad, 5 Ch.
Weller Street Housing Co-operative
Charles Dickens Centre, 7 Willow
Court, Wellerway, Liverpool L8 4XH.
Holyland Housing Co-operative
20 Parkhill Road, Liverpool L8.
•Cicely Housing Co-op *71 India House,*
75 Whitworth Street, Manchester
M1 6HB. 0161 228 2594. 2 Ad.
Birch Housing Co-op *17 Clitheroe Road,*
Longsight, Manchester M13 0GE.
0161 224 2011. 17 Ad, 12 Ch.
New Longsight Housing Co-operative
Studio 6, Imex Centre, Hamilton
Road, Longsight, Manchester
M13. 0161 256 4226. 150 Ad, 60 Ch.
Open House Housing Co-operative
60 Manley Road, Whalley Range,
Manchester M16 8HP. 40 Ad, 15 Ch.

Zah Housing Co-operative *36 Oak Road,*
Withington, Manchester M20 3DA.
0161 434 0339. 8 Ad, 1 Ch.
Commonplace Housing Co-op *20 Stockton*
Road, Chorlton, Manchester
M21 1LS. 0161 881 7839. 3 Ad.
New Barracks Tenants Management Co-op
1 Coronation Street, Ordsall,
Salford, Manchester M5 3SA.
0161 848 8256. 155 Ad, 150 Ch.
•Cloverhall Tenants Association Co-op
14 Farm Walk, Rochdale,
Lancashire OL16 2TN.
01706 350116. 260 Ad, 370 Ch.
Carrbrook Housing Co-Operative
1 Broadbent Close, Carrbrook,
Stalybridge, Manchester SK15 3LJ.
01457 832195.
Clay Brown Community Housing Association
44b Carfield, Digmoor, Skelmersdale,
Lancashire WN8 9HP.

HOUSING CO-OPS IN YORKSHIRE AND HUMBERSIDE

Giroscope Co-op
46 Wellstead Street, Hull
HU3 3AQ. 01482 223376.
Danes Tenants Co-operative
76 Dibsdane, Orchard Park Estate,
Kingston upon Hull.
Cracks Housing Co-operative
4 South View, High Bentham
LA2 7LJ. 01524 263120. 7 Ad, 2 Ch.
Parkwood Rise Tenant Management Co-op
2 Leyland House, Parkwood Rise,
Keighley, West Yorks BD21 4RG.
Halton Moor Estate Management Society
69 Ullswater Crescent, Leeds LS15 0BW.
Harry's Co-operative
8 Mexborough Avenue, Leeds
LS7 3EF. 0113 262 7786. 4 Ad.
Badger Housing Co-op
6 Reginald View, Leeds LS7 3HR.

0113 262 8812. 8 Ad.
301 Housing Co-op
Flat 7, 301 Chapeltown Road, Leeds
LS7 3JT. 10 Ad, 10 Ch.
Latch Housing Co-operative
138 Spencer Place, Leeds LS7 4DX.
0113 237 4482. 15 Ad, 6 Ch.
Alpha Tenant Management Co-op
14 Hyde Park Walk, Sheffield.
0114 275 7439. 233 Ad.
Maltby Housing Co-operative
57 Salisbury Road, Maltby, South
Yorks S66 7EZ. 01709 798777. 81 Ad.

SUPPORT ORGANISATION
Yorkshire CHS
c/o North Sheffield Housing Ass, 91
Spital Hill, Sheffield S4 7LD.

East Anglia

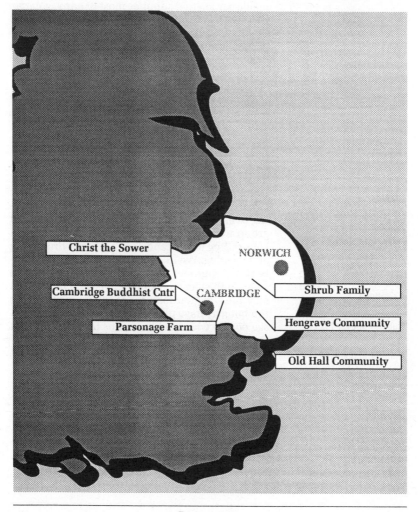

PARSONAGE FARM

Parsonage Farm is a community of nine adults and five children about 12 miles from Cambridge. We live in a large old house in three and a half acres of land at the edge of a large village. Most people have absorbing jobs outside the community so the main activity that brings us together is caring for the large organic vegetable garden that supplies most of our vegetarian diet (with occasional fish!). Every third weekend or so we work together with WWOOFers on the garden and we commit ourselves to one week a year of house maintenance. The community has a large Elizabethan barn where there is workshop space and the potential for development of other ideas. We eat together in the evening and support each other informally in childcare and life. The group is quite stable; the most recent member joined over four years ago and some members have been here over eighteen years. Some people here work in Delta T Devices, a co-operative business producing electronic research instruments. Delta T was formed by community members twenty years ago and is still going strong; employing twenty-six at the last count. We are a varied group with interests ranging from re-evaluation counselling to sea canoeing to African drumming and dancing. We like to relax together particularly in the summer when barbecues and trips to swim in the local brick pit (and cover ourselves in clay!) is a regular feature. At the moment we are full but may have places in the future. We encourage people who want to visit us to write and visit on a gardening weekend.

Status
existing community

Address
128 Low Road
Burwell
Cambridgeshire
CB5 0EJ

Telephone

Number of over 18s
9

Number of under 18s
5

Year started
1971

Situation
rural

Ideological focus
unfocussed

Open to new members?
No

A one hundred and twenty roomed main building. Thirty five adult members. Nineteen children and teenagers. Seventeen guests. A dozen cows, two ponies, fifty chickens, thirteen geese, about forty sheep, three bee hives, several cats, no dogs and sixty five acres of fertile land. Two tractors and an assortment of fittings, three trailers, ten wheelbarrows, a dumper truck, two four wheeled trolleys. One hundred and fifty windows, twenty two toilets, twenty eight wash hand basins, thirteen baths, ten showers, twenty sinks and all the associated plumbing fittings and pipe runs. Miles of electrical wiring. Two acres of roof coverings, guttering, down pipes, sewerage runs, manholes, land drainage, fencing, ditches. All this and more needs maintaining. In a year we grow, harvest, store and grind three acres of wheat from which we make fifty loaves of bread a week. We grow and consume 1500lbs of onions, three tons of potatoes, a ton of carrots, a ton of leeks, wheelbarrows full of tomatoes, courgettes, marrows, sweetcorn, green beans and so on. We pick, cook, store, freeze masses of soft fruit, apples, pears, plums, gooseberries, strawberries, raspberries, loganberries and the like. From the cows milk is made butter, cheese & yoghurt. This food is used to prepare, serve and consume upwards of thirty thousand communal meals a year. Then there is the washing up, the cleaning, the scrubbing, the gathering, chopping and stacking of seventy tons of wood a year for the space heating around the building. We do all this because we enjoy it. It is not work but fun. Pushing a trolley down a supermarket aisle picking cling film wrapped squeaky clean euro size sameness from the shelves is another life. Old Hall is a working example of Anarcho-Syndicalism. It has been for twenty one years now, though if you were to ask most members what Anarcho-Syndicalism was, they wouldn't have a clue.

OLD HALL COMMUNITY

Status
existing community

Address
East Bergholt
COLCHESTER
Essex
CO7 6TG

Telephone
01206 298045

Number of over 18s
48

Number of under 18s
22

Year started
1974

Situation
rural

Ideological focus
Green

Legal structure
Unincorporated

Open to new members?
Yes

HENGRAVE COMMUNITY

In a world where resources are unequally shared and often selfishly squandered the Hengrave Community of Reconciliation aims to live simply, committed to a life of sharing, prayer, work and play, goods, talents, interests, enthusiasm. All ages, denominations and nationalities are included as we seek to bridge the divisions in our global society. The inspiration of the community is extended in its work of running the Hengrave Hall Conference and Retreat Centre in a former Tudor manor house, welcoming people of all denominations or none.

Status
existing community

Address
Hengrave Hall Centre
BURY St EDMUNDS
Suffolk
IP28 6LZ

Telephone
01284 701561

Fax
01284 702950

Number of over 18s
20 - 25

Number of under 18s
0

Year started
1974

Situation
rural

Ideological focus
ecumenical

Legal structure
Registered Charity

Open to new members?
Yes

Shrub Family lives in an old cold 17th century farmhouse. We're surrounded by typical English countryside - intensively farmed wheat fields, a busy road and no hedges - rural but no idyll! It could be depressing but the underlying beauty of the area shines through - and as our primary concern is to explore ways of moving towards sensitive, economically and environmentally realistic rural development it's good to live with modern country conditions. Our dream is to get involved in building more space, preferably of low cost energy efficient housing and to this end we plan to convert to housing co-op status. We are relaxed, non-doctrinaire, like playing music, children, cats, good food, fun and conversation. There's no joining capital but members must commit one full working day a week to the needs of the house and grounds, contribute to running and maintenance costs and spend a minimum of eight weeks living here before they can become full members. Domestically we prefer to share household chores and at least one meal a day, avoid meetings, and look to build friendship, care and co-operation wherever possible. Visitors are welcome *by prior arrangement* and are asked to contribute £3.00 per day per person.

SHRUB FAMILY

Status
existing community

Address
Shrub Farm Cottages
Larling
East Harling
Norfolk
NR16 2QT

Telephone

Number of over 18s
5

Number of under 18s
5

Year started
1969

Situation
rural

Ideological focus
ecological

Legal structure
Co Ltd by Guarantee

Open to new members?
Yes

SOCIETY OF CHRIST THE SOWER

Three hundred and sixty years ago Little Gidding was the site of a Christian community led by Nicholas Ferrar, in which families and single people lived and worshipped together. Today it is the centre of the Society of Christ the Sower, which includes over 250 people from all Christian traditions, living at Little Gidding itself and scattered across Britain and the world. The tiny church at Little Gidding continues to attract countless pilgrims. Visitors are invited to Ferrar House where the Parlour is open daily from 2 to 5. Simple refreshments are served, and cards, books and gifts are for sale. Groups are welcome for a guided tour and refreshments. There are facilities for small groups to hold quiet days. There are four self-catering guest rooms. Guests are invited to the communal meal on Friday evening, to a celebration of the Lord's Supper on Saturday evening and to daily worship. All are welcome to explore joining the Society or living at or near Little Gidding. Those joining receive the Little Gidding Prayer Book to use in their own worship. They also receive a set of daily readings, a prayer calendar and a newsletter.

Status
existing community

Address
*Little Gidding
HUNTINGDON
PE17 5RJ*

Telephone
01832 293383

Number of over 18s
15

Number of under 18s
8

Year started
1981

Situation
rural

Ideological focus
Christian

Legal structure
Registered Charity

Open to new members?
Yes

CAMBRIDGE BUDDHIST CENTRE COMMUNITIES

Status

network

Address

25 Newmarket Road
CAMBRIDGE
CB5 8EG

The Cambridge Buddhist Centre is the public centre for Friends of the Western Buddhist Order to attend. The Centre has moved to new and bigger premises on Newmarket Road, a few doors up from the previous address. There are also five community houses - four men's and one women's - with altogether about 61 people living in them , all of whom are practising Buddhists. The first community in Cambridge was started in 1987 and more people have joined every year since. There are two businesses associated with the Centre, a wholesale business supplying jewellery and gifts to retailers, and a shop selling the goods. Many of the community residents work in the businesses. People who live in the Centre and work in the business receive a small income for personal items, and those who do not work in the business pay for board and lodging themselves. The communities are gradually expanding and the people who join come through their involvement with Buddhism. In communities members find it easier to put into practice the Buddhist principles of non-violence, truthful and gentle speech, friendship, mindfulness, simplicity and contentment. Being part of the spiritual community allows openness and trust to develop. Each house may organise itself slightly differently, but share certain features: a morning meditation together when possible and at least one evening a week shared together. At the moment there are no communities with children. Weekend retreats in country locations are organised regularly for the people coming to the mediattion or Buddhism classes at the Centre which are open to the public. These retreats allow a sampling of community living for a short period.

HOUSING CO-OPS IN EAST ANGLIA

Paradise Housing Co-operative
80 Kingston Street, Cambridge
CB1 2NU. 01223 560423. 11 Ad.
Argyle Street Housing Co-operative
3 Fletchers Terrace, Cambridge
CB1 3LU. 01223 411615.
87 Ad, 9 Ch.

The Midlands

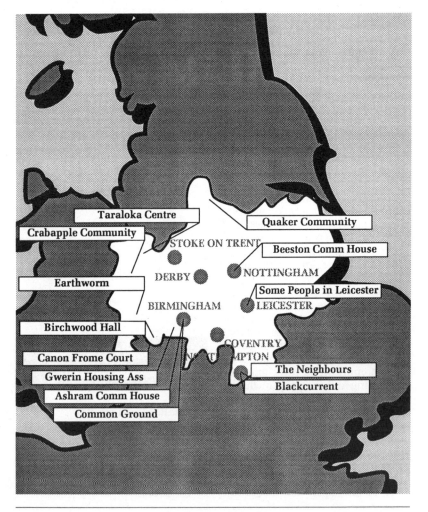

Nineteen of us - couples, singles, children - live in a converted former water board office. The families have separate units and most individuals have large bedsits. We have a communal kitchen/dining room, sitting room and facilities for people with disabilities on the ground floor. We provide respite care on a short-term basis. Quaker Meeting for Worship is held twice daily, morning and evening, and on Sundays at 10.30am as well. We encourage people to stay for a bring and share lunch after Meeting on the First Sunday of the month. We have no hierarchy and our decision making is along Quaker lines. Almost everyone has at least part-time work outside the Community and two members run businesses within it: a pottery and a wholefood delivery service. We are all involved in the life of the local wider community. We have seven acres of land which we are rehabilitating, using Permaculture principles, after 90 years of water board/railway use. It includes woodland, wetland, vegetables grown organically in raised beds, a forest garden and wildflower meadow. We are establishing a resource centre where people can get close to, and learn about, nature. Part of our nature trail is wheelchair accessible and a composting toilet is soon to be completed. Working weekends are held on the first and third weekends of each month - enquiries by post only, please, including a stamped addressed envelope. Sorry, but we do not have energy for visitors at other times.

QUAKER COMMUNITY, BAMFORD

Status
existing community

Address
Water Lane
BAMFORD
Derbyshire
S30 2DA

Telephone

Number of over 18s
15

Number of under 18s
4

Year started
1988

Situation
rural

Ideological focus
Quaker

Legal structure
Ind & Prov Society

Open to new members?
Yes

BEESTON COMMUNITY HOUSE

Beeston Community House is a Christian House situated near the centre of Beeston, Nottingham. There are six people living in the house and a number of others who share the aims and commitment but are non-residential. We come from different church backgrounds including Anglican, Baptist, Methodist and United Reformed Church. Each member of the house is a member of their own local church as well - we are not a house church. To describe who we are in words is difficult; living in Community House is a changing, moving experience. Most people stay for around three years although there is no rule. We are male and female, young and not so young; there are tears and laughter, good times and bad, but for this short part of our lives we are together, sharing our faith. The building was bought in 1975 by four 'senior' members of a local church who founded the Community based on four aims:

• to live together as an extended family
• to lead a life centred on prayer and worship
• to work for Unity in Christ among the local churches
• to have outreach in the wider local community

Over the years each fresh face of the Community has tried to work out for themselves what that means in practice ...

Status
existing community
Address
4 Grange Avenue
Beeston
NOTTINGHAM
NG9 1GJ
Telephone:

Electronic mail
oczjen@unicorn.
nottingham.ac.uk
Number of over 18s
6
Number of under 18s
0
Year started
1975
Situation
urban
Ideological focus
Christian
Legal structure
Registered Charity
Open to new members?
Yes

W e are a housing co-op with two houses in urban Northampton with seven members at present plus some part time children. We have weekly meetings where all decisions are made by consensus. We are founder members of Radical Routes, a secondary co-op. Our members are all vegetarian and we eat at least one meal a day communally. We have two halls which are used as workshops, meeting spaces for gatherings and occasional fayre type events. We also have allotment plots. We are all responsible for the maintenance of the buildings, accounts, raising of loan stock, administration etc. This involves a degree of skill sharing. An organic vegetable delivery service is run by some of us, and obviously we have our own interests as diverse as greenwood working, music, playing board games, saving the world and bad jokes. We have visitors weekends about once a month. All enquiries welcome.

BLACKCURRENT HOUSING CO-OP

Status
existing community

Address
24 St Michael's Avenue
NORTHAMPTON
NN1 4JQ

Telephone
01604 33203

Number of over 18s
9

Number of under 18s
0

Year started
1988

Situation
urban

Ideological focus
co-operation

Legal structure
Ind & Prov Society

Open to new members?
Yes

THE NEIGHBOURS

The Neighbours began in 1983 when two families bought three adjoining terrace houses and adapted them to form two households, an upstairs flat, and some shared accommodation. In 1985 a fourth house was added, and in 1987 a fifth. The gardens are combined into one large shared garden. It is an ecumenical group of lay people, who together constitute a "community of households", meeting together for worship each morning, for some meals, and seeking to support each other. We do not share income but have a common fund to which all contribute equally. In 1987 The Neighbours Trust was formed to offer financial support to people recovering from mental disorders, the householders being the Trustees. For some years our energies were directed towards offering support, and in some cases a home, to various people recovering in this way. More recently we have decided to move away from 'hands-on' care but we continue to place importance on hospitality as part of our common life. Our purpose is to develop a Christian community life which enables us to explore and share our faith and care for others according to the Gospel.

Status
existing community
Address
care of Diggers &
Dreamers
Telephone

Number of over 18s
9
Number of under 18s
4
Year started
1983
Situation
suburban
Ideological focus
Christian
Legal structure
Registered Charity
Open to new members?
Yes

SOME PEOPLE IN LEICESTER

Status
network

Address
care of
12 Bartholomew Street
LEICESTER
LE2 1FA

Telephone
0116 254 5436/1403

Fax
0116 255 5729

Some People in Leicester is a city based co-operative network with a variety of practical activities: co-operative work (electrical and building businesses; mail holding/photocopy service); vehicle sharing; shared childcare; organic gardening; income pooling; co-operative housing; capital pooling. Providing continuity is a smaller group of people (two at present but ideally three to five) intending a lifelong commitment to each other, based on sharing of emotional and financial resources. We call this the core group. We feel it is vital that the local groups do not exist in isolation but are involved in wider struggles and broader visions - our aim is to change the world! We are active members of Radical Routes Secondary Co-op - a network of radical housing and worker co-ops. Some of us are also working for people power - direct democracy, regional autonomy, recovering our lost history and culture. We welcome visitors by arrangement and are looking for more people to get involved.

HOUSING CO-OPS IN THE EAST MIDLANDS

Corani Housing And Land Co-operative
12 Bartholomew Street, Leicester LE2 1FA. 7 Ad, 2 Ch.

Belgrave Neighbourhood Co-op Housing Association
c/o LFHC, 131 Loughborough Road, Leicester LE4 5LQ. 116 266 6123. 441 Ad.

Cossington Housing Co-operative
c/o LFHC, 131 Loughborough Road, Leicester LE4 5LQ. 0116 266 6123. 194 Ad.

Ross Walk Housing Co-operative
c/o LFHC, 131 Loughborough Road, Leicester LE4 5LQ. 0116 266 6123.

Kutir Community Housing Co-operative
308a Melton Road, Leicester LE4 7AS. 0116 261 0459.

Cartergate Housing Co-operative
21 Cartergate, Nottingham, Nottinghamshire NG1 1EL. 0115 958 9270. 78 Ad.

Liberation Housing Co-operative
37 Burns Street, Radford, Nottingham NG7 4DS. 0115 978 7714. 5 Ad.

ASHRAM COMMUNITY HOUSE

Status
existing community

Address
23-25 Grantham Road
Sparkbrook
BIRMINGHAM
B11 1LU

Telephone
0121 773 7061

Fax
0121 772 4923

Number of over 18s
5

Number of under 18s
0

Year started
1977

Situation
urban

Ideological focus
Christian

Legal structure
Unincorporated

Open to new members?
Yes

Our mission statement is: "We are a radical Christian community, learning to live out our faith in shared lifestyle, joint action and through meeting Christ in others. Sparkbrook, a multi-racial, multi-faith, inner city area of Birmingham, has a predominately Pakistani Muslim population and is one of the poorest neighbourhoods in Britain, where racism and oppression are daily realities. We aim to be a Christian alternative living a simple lifestyle with a strong commitment to Muslim people. We seek to respond to inner city issues of poverty, marginalisation and environment. We aim to be a catalyst to draw people together to act for positive change at the roots, personally, in Sparkbrook and worldwide." In Practice this means: we are involved to greater or lesser degrees in activities aimed at meeting specific needs in the neighbourhood: eg community development and gardening on derelict land. Our door is generally open to visitors and volunteers of all backgrounds. We are self-supporting financially, sharing domestic tasks. We are looking for new members, please write or phone for details. (We are a branch of Ashram Community Trust - see their listing on page 207.)

Gwerin is a housing community, of five houses and a total of eighteen adults and three children. Four of the houses are part of a Victorian terrace and they are fairly large. These large houses are shared by members of our community. Each house is run differently according to the individuals who make up the household. We have weekly meetings where we all come together to discuss the running of the housing association. We are a mixture of individuals and as a community have no particular ideological focus, although a large number of us have contacts with the local Rudolf Steiner school.

GWERIN HOUSING ASSOCIATION

Status
existing community

Address
121 Hagley Road
STOURBRIDGE
West Midlands
DY8 1RD

Telephone
01384 396582

Fax
01384 396582

Number of over 18s
18

Number of under 18s
3

Year started
1980

Situation
urban

Ideological focus
none

Open to new members?
Yes

BIRCHWOOD HALL COMMUNITY

Status
existing community

Address
Storridge
MALVERN
Worcestershire
WR13 5EZ

Telephone

Number of over 18s
17

Number of under 18s
4

Year started
1970

Situation
rural

Ideological focus
socialist/feminist/green

Legal structure
Ind & Prov Society

Open to new members?
Yes

Birchwood Hall is a housing co-operative occupying two separate buildings. These operate as two separate entities, and the remainder of this description is concerned with the Main House group which currently consists of ten adults, one child, and one infant. Everyone here has paid employment, with some people working from home whilst others travel to Malvern, Worcester or Birmingham. Jobs are: Architect, designer, potter/audio-visual film-makers, civil servant, countryside ranger, milker, caterer, teacher, probation service worker, and University lecturer. Two college students also have Birchwood as their home, although they live away in term-time. We operate a degree of income sharing and children live here free. New members do not buy into the community, similarly they do not take out any money when they leave. The house is a large Victorian edifice which now contains communal spaces including living and dining area, kitchen, television room, games room, laundry, workshop, and office. Individuals have their own room or share with a partner - there is quite a lot of personal space. Everyone takes a turn in cooking and aims to provide for individual's likes and dislikes. The evening meal is the time when we all meet daily, and provides a regular point of contact for all members. Other shared pleasures include maintenance of the building and the sewage system, shopping, gardening, and cleaning, all tackled with varying degrees of enthusiasm. We have nine acres of land. It is very beautiful and a struggle to keep in order. The communal vegetable garden is more productive than it has been for a long time, but we do not intend to be self-sufficient. The group operates on regular weekly meetings - alternately "business" and "feelings". Decisions are reached by consensus and we all value harmony within the group. We live with each other because we like each other most of the time. Separately, the community operates a small residential conference centre known as Anybody's Barn, details of which can be obtained from the same address.

Canon Frome Court is a Georgian manor house including communal dining, sitting and meeting rooms, kitchens, guest rooms, a gym and swimming pool. Members live in separate households with prices approximating the local market. We don't have a shared ideological focus though there is a prevailing sympathy with green issues. We farm our land co-operatively and organically to produce a considerable proportion of our food. Stock includes cattle, sheep, goats, chickens and bees. We have a walled garden, large greenhouse, poly-tunnel and orchards. The farm is the reason most of us have chosen to live at Canon Frome. We take our food seriously, enjoying growing it and eating it! Communal activities include hosting events, eating together, craft activities and trips to the local pub. Members meet weekly to discuss and plan the many aspects of living here, making decisions by consensus. Working together and independently on communal tasks is what "community" means to us. We try to find a balance between the private and communal and depend on tolerance and flexibility to pursue our shared aims. It's not always easy but the successes are enormously satisfying and with every new member we become a slightly different community. It's never boring!

CANON FROME COURT

Status
existing community

Address
LEDBURY
Herefordshire
HR8 2TD

Telephone
01531 670745

Number of over 18s
29

Number of under 18s
21

Year started
1978

Situation
rural

Ideological focus
ecological

Legal structure
Ind & Prov Society and Charity

Open to new members?
Yes

EARTHWORM

Status
existing community

Address
Wheatstone
Leintwardine
CRAVEN ARMS
Shropshire
SH7 0LH

Telephone:
01547 540461

Number of over 18s
6

Number of under 18s
2

Year started
1990

Situation
rural

Ideological focus
ecological

Legal structure
Ind & Prov Society

Open to new members?
Yes

Earthworm Housing Co-op has lived and worked at Wheatstone since January 1989, the membership and direction of the co-op has gone through many changes in this time, but most of the original aims and ideals continue to be upheld. There are seven acres of fertile land set in a beautiful valley with a large rundown house and outbuildings. We aim to explore and promote ecological and sustainable lifestyles. We try to minimise our use of products involving human, animal and environmental exploitation. We are communally vegan and share a vegan kitchen. We welcome children and try to support home education. Household decisions are made by consensus at weekly meetings. We farm the land veganically - without the use of chemicals or animal products/labour. We have three vegetable and herb gardens providing food for ourselves and guests. We are planting trees and exploring permaculture and forest garden techniques. Eventually we hope to gain some income from our gardens, but there is still a lot of work to do re-claiming neglected land. We hope to use alternative energy and appropriate technology. We recycle as much waste as we can and now use composting toilets. Wood is used for cooking, heating and hot water and we eat organic food. Before our arrival the buildings had been vandalised and neglected; we have done a lot of restoration but accommodation is still very basic: the house being quite scruffy and conditions harsh in winter. We are always working towards a more energy efficient and comfortable home and working place. We have a large field and fully equipped campers/catering kitchen which is available to groups for camps, courses and workshops. We host several events ranging from a Permaculture courses to Green Gatherings. If you are interested in facilities, please contact us. Earthworm promotes and liases with Radical Routes, a national network of housing and workers' co-ops. We operate a loan stock system to raise money for restoring the property and expanding our projects.

Crabapple Community has lived at Berrington Hall for twenty years - twenty years of juggling the various needs of house, land, animals, shop and people; a process which is frustrating, fun, hard work, rewarding, relentless, satisfying, fascinating ... different things to different people in different moods.Essentially our community shifts to accommodate the needs of its members but we still hold to shared responsibility and decision making, organic farming and gardening, respect for others, the responsible use of resources. We believe in talking things through, our weekly meetings ramble over a wide range of issues: whether peacocks are too noisy, how to deal with the rising phone bill, who's doing what, when and how we feel about it. A 200 year old 20 acre home requires a lot of work as does our wholefood shop in Shrewsbury. We share the work and our income from the shop and various part-time jobs. We hope to broaden our income sources and contacts by holding more workshops and working weekends. We are open to visitors, a first visit is usually around four days. No capital is needed to join nor any specific skills. Most important is that we like living with you.

CRABAPPLE COMMUNITY

Status
existing community

Address
Berrington Hall
Berrington
SHREWSBURY
Shropshire
SY5 6HA

Telephone

Number of over 18s
6

Number of under 18s
1

Year started
1975

Situation
rural

Ideological focus
no single word

Open to new members?
Yes

TARALOKA BUDDHIST RETREAT CENTRE FOR WOMEN

Status

existing community

Address

Cornhill Farm
Bettisfield
WHITCHURCH
Shropshire
SY13 2LD

Telephone

01948 710646

Electronic mail

100073,3502
@compuserve.com

Number of over 18s

10

Number of under 18s

0

Year started

1985

Situation

rural

Ideological focus

Buddhist

Legal structure

Registered Charity

Open to new members?

No

Taraloka is both a community and a Buddhist retreat centre for women, to which women come from all over the world to experience the calm, beautiful atmosphere which has built up over the ten years of the centre's existence. The community exists to run the centre, each of its members playing a role in this. The community actively pursues the Buddhist way of life, following a daily programme of meditation, worship, work, communal meals. We also hold weekly business meetings and community meetings. Recently we have restructured our work situation by splitting into two teams, which meet daily to report-in and to plan each day's work. We have an admin. team and a retreat organising team. We aim to be friendly and co-operative and decisions are arrived at through consensus. We are constituted as a charity. There is no entry fee, although new prospective members pay their own way for the three months of their trial period. If they are accepted as members they receive basic support. Celibacy is observed by all members on the premises but there is no bar to sexual relationships outside. As part of our ethical practice we are all vegetarians. Further information from our secretary.

COMMON GROUND

Status
network

Address
24 South Road
Hockley
BIRMINGHAM
B18 5NB

Telephone
0121 551 1679

Fax
0121 515 3524

We are a group of housing and worker co-operative based in inner Birmingham. We are all involved in such activities as vegan and veggie outside catering (including festival catering), organic vegetable and wholefood distribution, organic veg. growing, computer serving, vehicle maintenance, house maintenance and home educating. At present we have 2 co-operative house in close proximity in which members share communally (to varying degrees). Other members live, though their own choice, in separate housing situations. We are in the process of buying further houses. We work closely together in order to maximise the potential for co-operation. We share resources i.e. vehicles, office space and equipment and labour. Most workers are waged by the businesses (we are aiming to pay wages to all workers). Becoming a member means the chance to learn new skills, through full training in your chosen areas of work and training in co-operative skills such as consensus decision making, facilitating meetings and mediation. Shared childcare is available and support for home-educating children. We are members of Radical Routes - a national secondary co-operative which provides support and services to its member co-ops, who are all committed to actively working towards social change.

HOUSING CO-OPS IN THE WEST MIDLANDS

Small Heath Park Housing Co-operative
15 Rochdale Walk, Cooksey Road, Birmingham B10 0DF. 0121 773 3251. 84 Ad.

Balsall Heath Housing Co-op
106 Alcester Road, Moseley, Birmingham B13 8HS. 0121 449 8661. 100 Ad.

Pavilion Housing Co-operative
572 Chester Road, Wylde Green, Sutton Coldfield, Birmingham B77 5HL. 0121 603 8410. 56 Ad, 4 Ch.

Chuckery Tenant Management Co-operative
2 Brookes House, Walsall, West Midlands WS1 2HS. 01922 644456 380 Ad.

Wissage Court Tenants Co-operative
10 Wissage Court, Trent Valley Road, Lichfield, Staffs WS13 6EH. 34 Ad, 6 Ch.

SUPPORT ORGANISATION
Birmingham CHS
510a Coventry Road, Small Heath, Birmingham B10 0UN. 0121 773 3583.

Wales

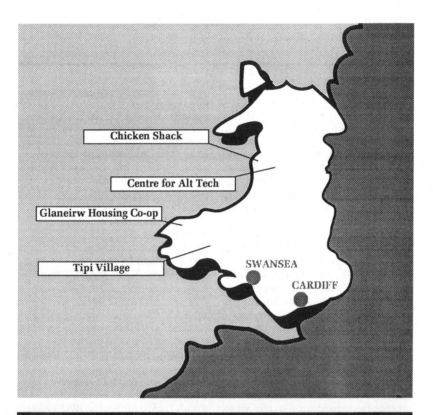

Chicken Shack

Centre for Alt Tech

Glaneirw Housing Co-op

Tipi Village

SWANSEA

CARDIFF

HOUSING CO-OPS IN WALES

SHAW Co-operative Housing Association
1 Lonks Court, Links Business Park,
St Mellons, Cardiff CF3 0LT.
01222 364411.

Newport Action For Single Homeless
20 Clarence Place, Newport, Gwent
NP? 0AE. 01633 211324.

Chicken Shack is a new housing co-op, financed by loans from the Radical Routes Secondary Co-op, Mercury Provident and our own loan stock issue. We are currently housing eight people at Brynllwyn, which is a Welsh farmhouse and two cottages set in four acres of the Snowdonia National Park.

CHICKEN SHACK HOUSING CO-OP

Our aims, beyond housing our members, are to explore and develop permaculture and other aspects of ethical living. We aim to support and promote the development of other housing and worker co-ops, as well as being active in the permaculture and alternative technology network. Part of our sustainable design includes developing a domestic reed bed and compost sewage system. As well as tree planting and establishing a land fund, we are exploring ways to utilise our existing wet land.

We welcome inquiries for information and offers of support in any of the above or related areas.

Status
existing community

Address
Brynllwyn
Rhoslefain
Tywyn
Gwynedd
LL36 9NH

Telephone

Number of over 18s
8

Number of under 18s

Year started
1994

Situation
rural

Ideological focus
ethical living

Open to new members?

CENTRE FOR ALTERNATIVE TECHNOLOGY

In addition to the exhibition and displays the Llwyngwern Quarry is also home to a small residential community, made up of people who work at the Centre for Alternative Technology

Status
existing community

Address
Llwyngwern Quarry
MACHYNLLETH
Powys
SY20 9AZ

Telephone
01654 702924

Fax
01654 702782

Number of over 18s
8

Number of under 18s
1

Year started
1975

Situation
rural

Ideological focus
pragmatism

Legal structure

Open to new members?

Structure: intentionally informal

Economic relations: life sustaining activities are funded jointly and equally except by people who are age challenged

Approaches to decision making: tangential and Kropotkinite except when something needs to be done

Childcare and education: we all play with the children until their parents come and take them away

Diet and eating habits: very low meat diet

Types of work: varied

Types of building and land: rural industrial reclaimed site with modified 19th Century industrial cottages plus some new build

Private space: we all have some

Legal structure: none

Special feature: tenancy is tied to working for the Centre for Alternative Technology

Postal enquiries: via the Centre for Alternative Technology only

The Tipi Village community is dedicated to living lightly upon the Earth and in harmony with the natural environment. We live in native North American style tipis in over 100 acres of Welsh hill land. Each tipi is an individual or family "household", so our community is very much a tribal village rather than a commune, but a village with a high component of communal activity and inter-action. Our land is partly owned by individuals and partly owned in trust on behalf of the community as a whole. We share a large tipi (the "Big Lodge") which functions as a communal space for parties, celebrations, get-togethers and (very rare) meetings, as well as accommodation for visitors and guests. We also share regular sweat lodges (saunas). We regard all of our land as a nature reserve in which humans can live in integrated harmony with nature. Formal structure and organisation are minimal, verging on non-existent, but we have a collective land fund to which all contribute in order to add, periodically, to our trust land holding. We have no hierarchy or elected authority, but long-standing members are regarded as tribal elders with organically developed rôles and influence. Decisions (when absolutely necessary) are made by consensus and enforced by collective social pressure. We have a co-operative extended tribal family attitude towards childcare. Most babies are born by natural home birth. Some children are home educated but an increasing number now attend local schools. We grow much of our own vegetables in individual and family organic gardens and (being dependent on firewood for fuel) we are particularly keen on tree planting. Visitors are welcome but dogs are definitely not and parking space for vehicles is strictly limited. Please send a stamped addressed envelope with all inquiries.

TIPI VILLAGE

Status
existing community

Address
Marchoglwyn Fawr
Llanfynydd
CARMARTHEN
Dyfed
SA32 7UQ

Telephone
01558 685066

Number of over 18s
80

Number of under 18s
50

Year started
1976

Situation
rural

Ideological focus
eco-pagan

Open to new members?
No

GLANEIRW COMMUNITY

Status
existing community

Address
Blaenporth
CARDIGAN
Dyfed
SA43 2HP

Telephone
01239 810548

Number of over 18s
3

Number of under 18s
3

Year started
1975

Situation
rural

Ideological focus
ecological

Legal structure
Ind & Prov Society

Open to new members?
Yes

Glaneirw is a small farm in west Wales with 44 acres of land and a large shabby house in which we live. We try to get most of our food and fuel from the land. There is a walled garden, and orchard and two polytunnels for vegetable and fruit growing. We keep cows, donkeys, chickens, ducks and geese. We have 5 acres of mature woodland and 8 acres planted since the commune began. There is a mortgage to pay so we have a business repairing, converting and supplying parts for Rayburn cookers, and a pottery workshop with our own shop. We pool our income and take weekly pocket money. Everyone has their own room but other rooms are communal. We share a meal every evening and have informal meetings every week. Housework, cooking and emptying the compost toilets, are also shared. New ventures for the year are bee-keeping and digging a drainage trench and reed bed, repairs to the buildings are ongoing. We enjoy having visitors but please write and make arrangements first. We are particularly interested in diggers and weeders, builders and alternative energy experts, but anyone with energy and humour will be welcome.

South West England

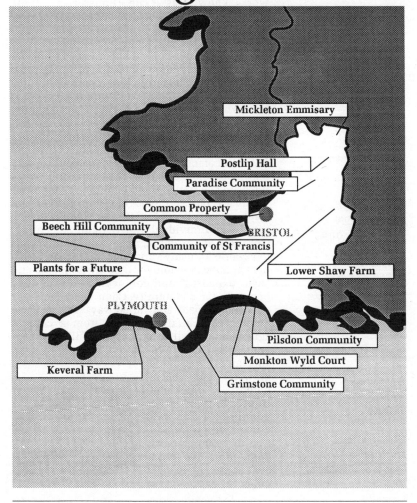

Mickleton Emmisary

Postlip Hall

Paradise Community

Common Property

Beech Hill Community

Community of St Francis

BRISTOL

Plants for a Future

Lower Shaw Farm

PLYMOUTH

Pilsdon Community

Monkton Wyld Court

Keveral Farm

Grimstone Community

MICKLETON EMMISARY COMMUNITY

Status
existing community

Address
Mickleton House
MICKLETON
Gloucestershire
GL55 6RY

Telephone
01386 438251

Fax
01386 438118

Number of over 18s
45

Number of under 18s
9

Year started
1980

Situation
village

Ideological focus
spiritual

Open to new members?
Yes

This is a long-standing community. Yet anyone looking primarily for a good community to live in is liable to be disappointed and should probably look elsewhere. Our main reason for being together is spiritual. What we do is very much of secondary importance to how we do it. We are part of a world-wide network known as 'The Emissaries", with sister-communities in many countries. We are the main Emissary community in Britain. Three times a week we meet for an hour or more to consider indepth our current experience of life. We also make regular use of a technique for spiritual "attunement". The focal point of our week is the meeting held at 11am every Sunday, which is always open to the public. Living in a community is not essential to our approach to life, but it is useful because it intensifies the pressure for change. Although there is a high level of love and fulfilment among us, this is also frequently a very uncomfortable place to be: the recipe only works if we are committed to maintaining, as far as we are able, a consistent sense of vision, purpose and stable atmosphere. Emissaries share a strong respect for individual integrity and perception. Our diets, for example, range from omnivorous to vegan with many variations. In finances, each person is responsible for their own income and basic expenses, and for deciding what they donate to the community. Communal decisions are made in many and varied ways. The management of our affairs emerges from a core of agreement. We all accept responsibility for generating that core. We are not farmers, or even substantial vegetable-growers: our central home, Mickleton House, is right in the middle of a Cotswald village with a population of 1,500 or more. Some of us live in our own homes, up to eight miles away.

We are a group of eight families who live together, in self-contained units in Postlip Hall, a large, beautiful, Jacobean manor house with fourteen acres of land in the Cotswolds, seven miles north-east of Cheltenham. Each family owns the leasehold on its individual unit, we all own the free-hold communally. Some parts of the main Hall and outbuildings, the fourteenth century Tithe Barn and the grounds are shared. The upkeep of the grounds, which included gardens, lawns, woodland, grazing for animals and a two-acre, walled, organic vegetable garden, and maintenance work on the Hall and Barn takes up a lot of our time. We come close to being self-sufficient in vegetables which, with the invaluable aid of WWOOFFers, are communally grown. Pigs, sheep, chickens, geese, ducks, rabbits, hamsters, cats and a Shetland pony are looked after by individuals or groups of members. Public events of all kinds are held in the Hall, Barn and grounds. The Cotswold Beer Festival is held here annually. From May to September the Barn and Hall are used for arts and craft exhibitions and sales, drama, concerts, weddings, parties, feasts, folk festivals and barn dances. Apart from the enjoyment, the events form a valuable source of income which helps to pay for the upkeep of the buildings and grounds which includes long-term restoration work on the listed Hall and Tithe Barn. Decisions are made at the monthly Housing Association meetings or in more informal discussions between members. We are a small community, but not a commune. Most of the adults earn our living outside Postlip, although we enjoy eating together two or three times a month, we live independent family lives. What draws us together is being with other people, joining in what the group decides to do for fun, profit or necessity, sharing our needs as and when necessary and just being at Postlip! You are welcome to visit but please arrange a convenient date with us first.

POSTLIP HALL

Status
existing community

Address
Winchcombe
near CHELTENHAM
Gloucestershire
GL54 5AQ

Telephone

Fax
01242 602237

Number of over 18s
16

Number of under 18s
15

Year started
1970

Situation
rural

Ideological focus
none

Legal structure
Unincorporated

Open to new members?
Yes

PARADISE COMMUNITY

Paradise Community is a place where people with special needs can live, learn and work on a long term basis. Founded on the well tried principles of Rudolf Steiner it pursues the ideals of compassion and self-help. Training and employment is offered in a variety of crafts, bio-dynamic gardening, farming and domestic work. A rich cultural life, meaningful leisure activities and care of houses and land form the fabric of a therapeutic environment, enhanced by regular observance of the Christian festivals. Resident staff work on a voluntary basis amd make community possible by their dedicated work. It is only possible to become a member by filling the post of house parent.

Status
existing community

Address
Paradise
PAINSWICK
Gloucestershire
GL6 6TN

Telephone

Fax
01452 812969

Number of over 18s
45

Number of under 18s
8

Year started
1976

Situation
rural

Ideological focus
Anthroposophy

Legal structure
Registered Charity

Open to new members?
No

The community, comprising three families, lives in a 200 year old listed farmhouse. Each family has its own living space but kitchen, bathrooms etc are shared. To earn a living the community runs a business in the farm's outbuildings, converted to meeting rooms and dormitaries, for up to 40 visitors. The business is weekend and week-long courses, educational and recreational, in a range of alternative, traditional and conventional activities (send a stamped addressed envelope for complete details). The farm (ex-dairy) is on the outskirts of Swindon and has goats, poultry, peacocks, a large organically run (and permaculture based) fruit and vegetable garden, a kindergarten, lots of local links, a national and international network of friends and supporters, regular meetings to ensure continuity and good order and a sense of humour. If you want to know more then write with a stamped addressed envelope.

LOWER SHAW FARM

Status
existing community

Address
Old Shaw Lane
Shaw
SWINDON
Wiltshire
SN5 9PJ

Telephone
01793 771080

Number of over 18s
7

Number of under 18s
7

Year started
1975

Situation
urban

Ideological focus
humanist/ecological

Legal structure
Unincorporated

Open to new members?
Yes

COMMON PROPERTY HOUSING CO-OP

The Old Vicarage is a large mock gothic Victorian town house in the centre of Bristol. It is encircled by a busy road, a church (now a thriving and sometimes noisy Community Centre), a library and a business park. We aim to be a haven amongst this inner city chaos. We are a housing co-op who have a long lease from Solon Housing Association. We have regular meetings to discuss co-op business, but many matters are discussed informally in the shared kitchen, the hub of the house. We live quite varied and independent lives, interests

Drawing of the Vicarage: Emma (aged 4)

Status
existing community

Address
The Old Vicarage
Trinity Road
Old Market
BRISTOL
BS2 0NW

Telephone

Number of over 18s
6

Number of under 18s
2

Year started
1981

Situation
urban

Ideological focus
Eclectic

Legal structure
Co Ltd by Shares

Open to new members?
Yes

include circus, storytelling, poetry, the arts, dance, science and environmental issues. We are all concerned about improving our society and environment and are committed to co-operative ideals. We run the house in a relaxed, sometimes haphazard manner. We are all involved in improving our skills and knowledge whether it be negotiating sound proofing, monitoring our finances, decorating, overhauling our large garden, group psychology or plumbing. We are a small co-op of six adult and two children. Livestock comprises two cats and two guinea pigs. We are interested in forming links with other co-ops and people who may be interested in joining us as occasional vacancies arise.

The Community of Saint Francis is an Active community in the Franciscan tradition in the Church of England. A commitment to regular corporate and personal prayer and study undergirds outreach of mission and caring work. At Compton Durville the sisters receive guests for rest, retreat and holidays: a large conference room is available for day groups or for projects. Other houses of the community are in urban priority areas where small groups of sisters are in part time semi-vocational, sometimes salaried work. The community has no major funds and members have to assist in generating sufficient income. As a registered charity there is no fixed charge for guests but a donation is requested. The sisters share a common dining room with guests and chapel services are open to all. Some spirituality programmes are offered from time to time; also individually guided reteats and Myers Briggs workshops. Community members make traditional religious vows of poverty, celibate chastity, and obedience, endeavouring to live these out in an open spirit of life sharing and relationships. Decision-making is mutual, consultative and where possible, by consensus. An elected chapter and officers operate as appropriate.

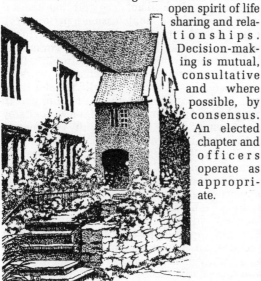

COMMUNITY OF ST FRANCIS

Status
existing community

Address
Compton Durville
SOUTH PETHERTON
Somerset
TA13 5ES

Telephone
01460 240473

Number of over 18s
15

Number of under 18s
0

Year started
1905

Situation
rural, but other houses in cities

Ideological focus
Christian

Legal structure
Registered Charity

Open to new members?
Yes

PILSDON COMMUNITY

We are dedicated to the ideals of the Christian Gospel in the context of community living and open hospitality. The Community at any one time will comprise of 5-7 community members (leadership role), plus children, 20-25 guests (1 month to several years), up to 6 visitors (1 day to 2 weeks) and up to 10 Wayfarers (1-3 days). Many of the guests have

Status
existing community

Address
Pilsdon Manor
BRIDPORT
Dorset
DT6 5NZ

Telephone
01308 868308

Number of over 18s
35

Number of under 18s
5

Year started
1958

Situation
very rural

Ideological focus
Christian

Legal structure
Registered Charity

Open to new members?
Yes

experienced a crisis in their lives (e.g. mental breakdown, alcoholism, drug addition, marital breakdown, abuse, homelessness, prison, drop out of school or college etc). Pilsdon provides a working therapeutic environment of communal living, manual work, creative opportunities (pottery, art, crafts, music etc) recreation, worship and pastoral care, to help re-build peoples lives, self-respect, confidence and faith. Founded in 1958 by an Anglican priest and his wife - Percy and Gaynor Smith - the Community occupies an Elizabethan manor house and its outbuildings in a valley in West Dorset, 6 miles from the sea. We farm nine and a half acres with a large kitchen and flower garden. Our life is inspired by the monastic tradition adapted by the seventeenth century Community of Little Gidding involving families, children and single men and women. The worship and spirituality is Anglican and sacramental, but ecumenical in membership. Community members are Christian, but all faiths and races and none are welcome. Membership, guests and visitor enquiries to the Warden.

Monkton Wyld is an holistic education centre and registered charity run by a group of 18 members and volunteers with three to five children. The setting is a neo-gothic Victorian rectory and outbuildings placed in a beautiful Dorset valley three miles from the sea. There are eleven acres of grounds which comprise a small farm providing milk, eggs, cheese and yoghurt, a one acre organic vegetable garden, lawns, children's play area, woods and stream. The rectory houses up to 34 guests and includes two large group rooms, Piano Room, Library, Meditation Hut, Sauna, Massage and Healing Room, Pottery and arts and crafts facilities; and also a Kindergarten and Toddler Group. We attune at 9.15am, have regular business meetings run through consensus and "contact" meetings to aid communication. We are an intentionl community and try to treat each person as individual and unique. Our income is generated through a full programme of courses running all year round including regular dancing and drumming classes. We entertain up to 2000 guests a year which provides the business income and our pocket money. We are always open to volunteers but at present are looking for new members (no capital required) who can make a serious commitment of two years (or more) with skills in maintenance, finance, gardening, administration and household. Telephone or write for more information and our brochure.

MONKTON WYLD COURT

Status
existing community

Address
Monkton Wyld
Charmouth
BRIDPORT
Dorset
DT6 6DQ

Telephone
01297 560342

Number of over 18s
16

Number of under 18s
3

Year started
1982

Situation
rural

Ideological focus
none

Legal structure
Registered Charity

Open to new members?
Yes

GRIMSTONE COMMUNITY

Status
existing community

Address
Grimstone Manor
Horrabridge
YELVERTON
Devon
PL20 7QY

Telephone
01822 854358

Number of over 18s
6

Number of under 18s
3

Year started
1990

Situation
rural

Ideological focus
New Age

Legal structure
Unincorporated

Open to new members?
Yes

Grimstone Community was formed to buy and develop the existing successful workshop centre at Grimstone Manor. A magical spot on the edge of Dartmoor, it is set in 27 acres of garden, pasture and wilderness. Members make a financial investment in the property and join the business partnership. We are six adults and three children. Recently two families have become affiliated members, investing money as non-residential co-owners of the property, but not participating in the business. Our main focus as a community is service to the many and varied therapy and development groups who come to work in, receive and feed the special energies here. We meet once a week alternating business and process meetings. All decisions are taken by consensus between equal partners. Members localise different areas of work, but generally all work is shared and paid at the same hourly rate. Short term volunteers work in return for their keep. We are moving towards building a sense of community on material, emotional and spiritual levels. Together we eat daily, meditate weekly, laugh, work and grow. There are local community links through circle dancing, chanting and other events. We are open to new members with capital, flexibility and enthusiasm.

Beech Hill is a spacious country house set in the rural heart of Devon. There are also a number of outbuildings converted for living in and for projects of interest to the co-op. We have seven acres of grounds and gardens. All cultivation is organically based and is largely focused upon production of a wide variety of vegetables and fruits. We have a young vineyard, a plant nursery, an ancient walled garden and a large paddock. A new purpose-built course centre, due to open in the Autumn of 1995, will provide accommodation and facilities for paying guests and groups. Some of us earn a living outside and some work within the co-operative. However, we are all involved, to a greater or lesser extent, in the co-op's overall plans and projects. To live here happily and effectively, people need goodwill, personal initiative, tolerance and stability. Dogmatism and preaching are definitely not wanted. Our intention is to go beyond narrow definitions of party politics, religious tradition and social structure. By thinking and acting co-operatively, we create unusual opportunities - for ourselves and for others - which improve the real quality of being and also enhance the circumstances in which we live. The co-operative's aims are summed up as follows: • To achieve maximum flexibility for individuals within collective policies • To enable people to use and develop skills • To provide a meeting place where people can share ideas, information and experience • To create structures and opportunities which maximise possibilities within the current social and economic climate • To be aware of the impact of our work and lives on the environment and to develop projects accordingly. At Beech Hill we aim to be a happy blend of rural peace and liveliness, honest work and restful leisure, philosophy and fun. We welcome visitors and ask that they write a short note about themselves (interests, background, etc) before coming. We will then send out further details about Beech Hill, together with suggested visiting dates.

BEECH HILL COMMUNITY

Status
existing community

Address
Beech Hill House
Morchard Bishop
CREDITON
Devon
EX17 6RF

Telephone
01363 877228

Number of over 18s
16

Number of under 18s
3

Year started
1983

Situation
rural

Ideological focus
ecological

Legal structure
Co Ltd by Guarantee

Open to new members?
Yes

PLANTS FOR A FUTURE

We are a group of people in the process of setting up a village style community. We have 28 acres of land and hope to obtain planning permission to live on it as soon as possible. We believe that plants can provide us with most of our needs without us having to exploit animals in any way. We have information on computer of over 6,000 species of plants that can be grown outdoors in Britain and can provide us with food, fuel, cloths, medicines, building materials and more. We are growing over 1,500 of these species and have planted almost 20,000 trees over the last five years. We can supply people with plant information and with young plants. We try to make all decisions by consensus if possible and have various communal events such as music, yoga and circle dancing. We would welcome new members. However, we have no spare accommodation here at the moment. Likewise we have no spare room to put up visitors most of the time. If you would like to visit us, though, give us a ring and it may be possible to fit you in when one or more of us are away.

Status
existing community

Address
The Field
Higher Penpol
St Veep
LOSTWITHIEL
Cornwall
PL22 0NC

Telephone
01208 873554/623

Number of over 18s
15

Number of under 18s
5

Year started
1990

Situation
rural

Ideological focus
vegan, ecological anarchism, co-operation

Legal structure
Co Ltd by Guarantee & Charity

Open to new members?
Yes

Keveral Farm is an organic farm community comprising farmhouse, farm buildings and 30 acres of land. Extra dwelling space is provided by caravans and benders. The house is the focus of community life, with communal rooms, shared meals, social space and meeting space. Keveral is currently owned by Patchwork Housing Association but we are negotiating to buy it off them. This will require a lot of fundraising followed by a lot of renovation work but should provide a good focus and incentive for working together and establishing long term objectives. We have a housing co-op to run the house, and a worker co-op to run the farm. Most of us are unemployed and work on the farm is voluntary. We occasionally get paid work in the outside world but hope eventually to make a living from our activities on the farm. Many people have their own personal projects and priorities, such as: growing food; woodland management; co-ordinating the local LETS scheme, running a metal workshop, childcare and just living.

We have just introduced Communal Workdays to bring us together more, though we are relying heavily on visitors and volunteers to help with our horticulture. This is done mostly in our four polytunnels, but we also have a walled garden and other outdoor growing areas. Our goats and chickens are now kept to be productive rather than as pets. We have eight acres of woodland, a young orchard, and we are establishing new areas of woodland. We are working towards an integrated farm plan, including a more eco-friendly house. We are establishing a camping area for groups and individuals; and also farm trails and educational facilities. We have a "Visitors' Barn" for courses, workshops and parties. Keveral has a very scenic and tranquil location, only 15 minutes walk from the beach (and pub!) and on fine summer days is more like a holiday camp ... but winds, rain and mist rolling in from the sea make us sometimes wish we were not living on top of a hill!

KEVERAL FARM COMMUNITY

Status
existing community

Address
Keveral Farm
Seaton
near LOOE
Cornwall
PL13 1PA

Telephone
01503 250215

Number of over 18s
14

Number of under 18s
3

Year started
1973

Situation
rural

Ideological focus
sustainability

Legal structure
Co Ltd by Guarantee

Open to new members?
Yes

AVALON

Status

embryonic community

Address

*care of 30 Video Court
2 Mountview Road
Finsbury Park
LONDON
N4 4SJ*

Telephone

0181 341 3671

Intended Situation

semi rural

Ideological focus

Spiritual

We are an embryonic community with a vision of a new kind of home for older people - neither an old people's home nor a monastery - but a retirement home with a spiritual focus. We realise that most of our lifetimes are spent in the act of doing, getting and holding on. Old age, by contrast, comes to teach us the art of letting go. We are seeking to set up our contemplative community home somewhere in England, probably in the West Country. As most residents will be of retirement age, we want to provide space and facilities for residents to receive nursing care within the community. We are considering various financial options and ideally we want the flexibility to accommodate both people who would prefer to pay capital and people who want to pay rent. If you are interested in joining our community, either as a resident in the near future, or with a longer term view to securing a place for later life, we would like to hear from you. We particularly want to encourage people who are not yet approaching retirement age to invest in the home for the future.

HOUSING CO-OPS IN SOUTH WEST ENGLAND

Bath Housing Co-op
*23 Bennett Street, Bath, Avon
BA1 2QL. 01225 339105. 30 Ad.*
Bristol Youth Housing Co-operative
*Dings House, Oxford Street, St
Philip's, Bristol BS2.
0117 941 1465. 7 Ad.*
**Somewhere Co-operative Housing
Association**
*25 Dean Lane, Southville, Bristol ,
Avon BS3 1DB. 0117 940 9856.
18 Ad, 7 Ch.*

SUPPORT ORGANISATION
Great Western Region CHS Ltd
*23 Bennett Street, Bath, Avon
BA1 2QL. 01225 429309.*

South East England

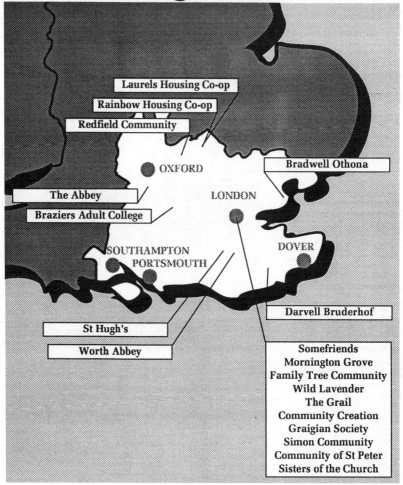

Laurels Housing Co-op

Rainbow Housing Co-op

Redfield Community

OXFORD

Bradwell Othona

The Abbey

LONDON

Braziers Adult College

SOUTHAMPTON
PORTSMOUTH

DOVER

Darvell Bruderhof

St Hugh's

Worth Abbey

Somefriends
Mornington Grove
Family Tree Community
Wild Lavender
The Grail
Community Creation
Graigian Society
Simon Community
Community of St Peter
Sisters of the Church

BRADWELL OTHONA COMMUNITY

Small core community now being established. Providing atmosphere of honest acceptance and an environment where faith and life can be studied with a view to more positive action in world affairs. Hope to promote deeper understanding of our multi-faith society. Live together in one building, own room. Possible work part/full time locally but commitment need-

Status
existing community

Address
Bradwell on Sea
SOUTHMINSTER
Essex
CM 0 7PN

Telephone

Number of over 18s
250

Number of under 18s
150

Year started
1946

Situation
rural

Ideological focus
Christian

Legal structure
Registered Charity

Open to new members?
Yes

ed to the aims of community. Interpersonal decisions decided one to one, other decisions dealt with by committee structure of elected members. Rural position isolated by sea, new and old buildings. Environmentally interesting site. Own reed-beds, electricity. Wish to promote use of available land, not good quality. Fluctuating numbers over a year, peaks Christmas, Summer, from outer members(?) Must be able to cope with variety of ages, faiths, nationalities. No facilities for childcare on site, local school nearby. Disabled facilities, share cooking, cleaning, maintenance tasks. Willing to respond to inquiries from applicants by letter.

The Laurels is a hundred year old building which used to be a Doctor's surgery. It was converted into a housing co-op in 1982. The house is now owned by Milton Keynes Borough Council who rent it out to us. There are eight private rooms, shared kitchen and living areas, workshop and a big beautiful garden, half of which is run by four chickens and the other half given over to flowers and artworks. We also have a separate allotment where we grow our veg. Members share the work involved in the running of the co-op. We have monthly meetings and elect a Treasurer and Secretary annually. We try to achieve consensus on making decisions. Some of us are vegetarians - we eat communaly once a month before our meetings.

LAURELS HOUSING CO-OPERATIVE

Status
existing community

Address
64 High Street
New Bradwell
MILTON KEYNES
Buckinghamshire
MK13 0BP

Telephone
01908 225769

Number of over 18s
6

Number of under 18s
4

Year started
1982

Situation
urban

Ideological focus
co-operation

Legal structure
Unincorporated

Open to new members?
Yes

RAINBOW HOUSING CO-OPERATIVE

Status
existing community

Address
9 Spencer Street
New Bradwell
MILTON KEYNES
MK13 0DW

Telephone
01908 670073

Number of over 18s
33

Number of under 18s
20

Year started
1977

Situation
urban

Ideological focus
green, co-operative
fundamentalists

Legal structure
Ind & Prov Society

Open to new members?
Yes

Rainbow is a fully mutual housing co-operative. We bought the houses from Milton Keynes Development Corporation. In 1977 a group of alternatively minded people took advantage of MKDC's policy of encouraging mixed housing stock by setting up a management co-op in 24 railway cottages. The government's 'right to buy' policy allowed us to buy the houses at a discount in 1992. One of the houses is a community house containing a laundrette, an office, a well equipped workshop and a meeting room. The co-op has about a third of an acre of land with a poly-tunnel, fruit trees, ducks, chickens and children's play area. Individuals can choose how collectively they wish to live, some people cook and eat together regularly or share child care; others live more privately but still use the shared facilities and attend meetings. We are run by a general meeting once a month plus subgroups for day-to-day organisation. We try to reach decisions by consensus, members range in age from zero to 65, meetings are open. Applying for a house is open to all ... but prospective members can expect a long wait for a house.

We are a community of 15 adults and 12 children living in a large 'country house' in rural Buckinghamshire. The buildings are set in 17 acres of gardens, fields and both mature and recently planted woodland.

Redfield is in its 19th year and that time has seen a growing commitment to communal living. We live as a single household, eat together every day and share all the domestic tasks and work on the estate. Much of our food comes from the gardens and the animals we keep. We use both organic and permaculture techniques. The woods provide fuel and include forest garden areas and both hazel and ash coppice.

Decision-making is by consensus of all the members at the weekly meetings where our various activities are co-ordinated. We also spend part of this time sharing news and feelings about issues within the group. One meeting every month has no agenda and is given over to exploring and celebrating different aspects of our life as a community.

There are several different ways to visit us. Local people often use our facilities or join in our regular music and dancing sessions. The Redfield Centre is a conference facility used by many outside groups throughout the year. We also have regular open days. For anyone who wishes further experience of communal life we welcome paying visitors for longer periods by arrangement.

Spending so much time together throws up lots of personal and collective challenges. Working through these can be both rewarding and inspiring. We all feel that what we get from this way of life is directly proportional to what we put into it.

REDFIELD COMMUNITY

Status
existing community

Address
Buckingham Road
Winslow
BUCKINGHAM
MK18 3LZ

Telephone
01296 713661

Fax
01296 714983

Electronic mail
redfield@gn.apc.org

Number of over 18s
15

Number of under 18s
12

Year started
1978

Situation
rural

Ideological focus
sustainability

Legal structure
Ind & Prov Society

Open to new members?
Yes

THE ABBEY

Status
existing community

Address
*The Green
Sutton Courtenay
ABINGDON
Oxfordshire
OX14 4AF*

Telephone
01235 847401

Fax
01235 847608

Number of over 18s
6

Number of under 18s
0

Year started
1982

Situation
rural

Legal structure
Registered Charity

Open to new members?
Yes

The Abbey is rooted in the Christian tradition, yet open to the wisdom of other faiths and to the challenge of the modern world. The Abbey Sutton Courtenay is a Community and a Conference/Retreat Centre, recognising the sacred dimensions in all areas of life. The Community consists of both resident and non-resident members carrying forward the vision of its founders "to re-discover Christ" in the context of today's modern society. It's everyday life is based on what it perceives as the four right relationships: to God, to the earth, to ourselves and to others. The Abbey's programme provides the opportunity to explore each of these relationships through retreats, inter-faith dialogue, healing work and day and weekend courses, focusing on such subjects as ecology, alternative economics and politics, the arts, non-violence and energy. The small resident community attempts to live out these four right relationships by living together co-operatively, simply and ecologically, and by sharing regular time for meditation and worship. The community also cares for a large and historically interesting fourteenth century house with rooms available to other groups and a library which includes most of Gandhi's published works. There are four acres of grounds, including a walled organic vegetable garden and a guest annexe which accommodates up to 14. The resident community meets regularly with members of the Council of Management to ensure the smooth running of both business and human aspects of the Abbey, and well as forwarding the vision of its founders, and late Fred J Blum and the now retired Bishop Stephen Verney.

Braziers is a resident community and a non-resident network of interested associates and members. It was founded in 1950 as a registered Friendly Society with the official title of "Braziers Park School of Integrative Social Research". The main aim is to carry out group research into positive health and holistic living, seeking new ways of working and thinking together which could offer hope of further human progress. As part of this research and, at the same time, to have a constructive social activity which helps provide an added source of income for the group, its facilities and amenities are made open to the public as a residential adult education college for weekend seminars and summer schools. Such courses, besides exploring subjects which can further the aim of social research, provide opportunities for people to learn and develop new insights and leisure skills. In this capacity Braziers is a member of the Adult Residential Colleges Association. The community regularly includes a number of British and overseas student volunteers who, during four decades, have helped establish Braziers as an international education centre with a reputation which reaches to many parts of the world. We should add that, besides a large house and some cottages the community is responsible for some 50 acres (26ha) including an organic garden and home farm. The produce helps make the community partly self-sufficient. Despite initial difficulties such as threaten any new social venture - including having to encounter and transcend schismatic trends - the community has been able, slowly, to work out new methods of democratic communication and structure, guided when ever possible by knowledge available from sociology, social psychology and the understanding of psycho-social evolution. From our experience has emerged a method of self-counselling and self governance which Braziers calls "the sensory-executive synthesis". Booklets and research papers which record and explain the method are available on sale from Braziers.

BRAZIERS ADULT COLLEGE

Status
existing community

Address
Braziers Park
Ipsden
WALLINGFORD
Oxfordshire
OX9 6AN

Telephone
01491 680221

Number of over 18s
13

Number of under 18s
2

Year started
1950

Situation
rural

Ideological focus
evolutionist

Legal structure
Friendly Society

Open to new members?
Yes

ST HUGH'S CHARTERHOUSE

Status
existing community

Address
Partridge Green
HORSHAM
West Sussex
RH13 8EB

Telephone
01403 864231

Fax
01403 864231

Number of over 18s
22

Number of under 18s
0

Year started
1873

Situation
rural

Ideological focus
Prayer

Open to new members?
Yes

Founded by Saint Bruno, 11th century Order of Carthusians (O. Cart) ~ Saint Hugh's opened in 1873 ~ Many Carthusian monasteries were destroyed in the 16th and 17th centuries ~Open only to males, minimum age 22. Must be babtized, confirmed, Roman Catholic ~ Solitary, prayerful life ~ silence essential: no radios, TVs, newspapers ~ One meal daily ~ Females (even infants) not permitted inside Charterhouse (strict enclosure) ~ Candidates come form all over the world ~ "Success" rate low (1 in 40) ~ Ability to remain quiet, work steadily and remain stable essential ~ Fathers wear hair shirts, not mandatory for brothers ~ Brothers have more of a community life than fathers ~ Broken sleep: 12.30 am - church for about 3 hours; next rise 7.00 am; mass 8.15 am - 1 hour; last prayer time communally in church - vespers - half an hour. Carthusian monasteries (Charterhouses) in Europe including five of O. Cart nuns; 1 in Vermont, USA. Candidates must be suited to this life. It is for very few. All must be chaste, prayerful, silent and have a deep love of our Lord Jesus Christ, and be willing to grow in that love for unselfish reasons. Self-denial and a spirit of obedience and povert (total dependence on God's grace as opposed to self-sufficiency) must be part of the candidates self-realisation. * Visitors are not encouraged unless tey intend to join us or are relatives of monks - whose families may visit them for 3 days once a year.

A group of students came to Worth Abbey in 1971 with an enthusiastic desire to share in the life and prayer of the monastic community. The monks offered them a building within the grounds which is now a centre for retreats and community living, run by lay people. The Lay Community is strongly rooted in the Christian Benedictine tradition and enables peo-

WORTH ABBEY LAY COMMUNITY

ple from different backgrounds to meet and pray together. It is an open and accepting community which gives a freedom to talk of God in a non-threatening and relaxed way. We warmly welcome you to come and stay at Worth for a weekend. It is a chance to take part in the balance of the Benedictine way of life which includes prayer, work and community life. There are also opportunities for living in the Lay Community. Whilst living in community you will share in the daily rythm of services with the monks. Residents are encouraged to continue outside employment, find local work or work full-time within the community. The Lay Community has grown to include over 400 members throughout the country and abroad. Members are linked to each other by regular visits to Worth and meeting in their own homes.

Status
existing community

Address
Worth Abbey
Turners Hill
CRAWLEY
West Sussex
RH10 4SB

Telephone
01342 715529

Fax
01342 718298

Number of over 18s
5

Number of under 18s
0

Year started
1971

Situation
rural

Ideological focus
Benedictine

Legal structure
Registered Charity

Open to new members?
Yes

DARVELL BRUDERHOF COMMUNITY

Status
existing community

Address
Hutterian Brethren
ROBERTSBRIDGE
East Sussex
TN32 5DR

Telephone
01580 881003

Fax
01580 881171

Number of over 18s
175

Number of under 18s
150

Year started
1920

Situation
rural

Ideological focus
Christian

Open to new members?
Yes

The Bruderhof Community began in Germany in 1920 just after the First World War, when Eberhard and Emmy Arnold with their five children moved to the village of Sannerz from their comfortable home in Berlin, to start a life of radical discipleship. Our roots go back 460 years to the Anabaptist movement, indeed to the Early Christians of the first 200 years AD and we seek to live like them. There are Bruderhof Communities in England and in the United States. Membership requires a lifetime commitment. Our first call is to Christ and this cannot be separated from the brothers and sisters to whom we are pledged. We do not feel that any one pattern for daily life is the answer, but we do believe in a life of Christian brotherhood that is the fruit of an inner change of heart. Our desire is to follow Jesus in the spirit of purity and humility in every aspect of life. Bruderhof children are educated in our own schools up to high school age. Training beyond that age is received outside the community, in most instances. The principal means of livelihood is our manufacturing - Community Playthings, nursery school equipment and Rifton Equipment for the Disabled. In addition, our non-profit Plough Publishing House offers a diverse selection of books, cassettes and videos covering all aspects of Christian discipleship and life in Christian community. Write for our free quarterly, The Plough. Inquiries are welcomed. Visits can be arranged but please write or call in advance so as to ensure accommodation. Guests are asked to share in the work and life in an open and seeking way. Our urgent longing and hope is that all men and women on this Earth will one day live in true justice and brotherhood under the rulership of God.

HOUSING CO-OPS IN SOUTH EAST ENGLAND

Two Piers Housing Co-operative
*14 Oriental Place, Brighton, East
Sussex BN1 2LJ. 01273 739779.
66 Ad, 15 Ch.*
Lorgan Housing Co-operative
*c/o Unemployed Centre, 6 Tilbury
Place, Brighton, East Sussex BN2
2GY. 01273 622791. 12 Ad, 2 Ch.*
Hecate Women's Housing Co-operative
*c/o Brighton Area CDA, 42 Baker
Street, Brighton, East Sussex
BN1 4JN. 10 Ad.*
Brighton Diggers Housing Co-op
*No 4 The Diggers, Golf Drive,
Brighton, East Sussex BN1 6AH.
01273 707855. 11 Ad, 7 Ch.*
Watch This Space Housing Co-operative
*Rooms 1 & 2, 128 Hollingbury Park
avenue, Brighton, East Sussex
BN1. 01273 696307. 27 Ad, 12 Ch.*
Brighton Rock Housing Co-op *399 Kings-
way, Hove, East Sussex BN3 4QE.*
Caburn Housing Co-operative *68 Western
Road, Lewes, East Sussex BN7 1RP.*
Group 11 Housing Co-operative
*The Old Surgery, 15a Station Road,
Epping, Essex CM16 4HG.
01992 560007.*
Roxborough Housing Co-operative
*18 Becker Road, Colchester, Essex
CO3 5XR.*
Milldale Housing Co-operative
*16 Milldale Close, Deal, Kent CT14 9UJ.
01304 369368. 79 Ad, 25 Ch.*
ABSE Housing Co-operative
*Little Grove, Grove Lane, Orchard
Leigh, Chesham, Buckinghamshire
HP5 3QL. 01494 782720. 14 Ad.*
Great Expectations Housing Co-operative
*26 Frindsbury Road, Strood,
Rochester, Kent ME2 4TB.*

Shenley Church End Housing Co-op
*5 Burchard Crescent, Shenley
Church End, Milton Keynes.*
Southsea Self-Help
*57 Lucknow St, Portsmouth PO1 1PT.
01705 870050. 52 Ad, 11 Ch.*
Spithead Housing Co-operative
*72 Victoria Road North, Southsea,
Portsmouth, Hampshire PO5 1QA.
01705 756068. 46 Ad, 2 Ch.*
Bradwell Common Housing Co-op
Rutherford Gate Housing Co-operative
*(Milton Keynes), c/o CDS,
207 Waterloo Road, LONDON
SE1 8XW. 0171 401 3131.*
Gemini Housing Co-operative
*136 Fairview Road, Stevenage,
Hertfordshire SG1 2NS. 30 Ad, 6 Ch.*
Sishes Housing Co-operative
*136 Fairview Road, Stevenage,
Hertfordshire SG1 2NS. 103 Ad, 0 Ch.*
Wisden Housing Co-operative
*1 Bader Close, Stevenage,
Hertfordshire SG1 5LA. 100 Ad.*
Northborough Housing Co-operative
*101 Pevensey Rd, Slough, Berkshire.
01753 534452. 120 Ad, 12 Ch.*
Mushroom Housing Co-operative
*33 St Mary's Road, Southampton,
Hampshire SO2 0BG.
01703 235108. 7 Ad, 1 Ch.*
Hamwic Housing Co-operative
*Exmoor House, Methuan Street,
Southampton, Hampshire
SO2 0SQ. 01703 232588. 60 Ad.*

SOMEFRIENDS COMMUNITY

Somefriends is an inner-city community constituted as a co-op. There are several ideals which have helped shape the community, including non violence, feminism, anti-racism, a concern for the environment, a concern for a spiritual perspective on life and vegetarianism. The definition and application of these ideas varies from member to member and there are few statements that can be made about this group as a whole on any of these ideas. We are constantly exploring the tension between finding our own space and sharing our lives with each other. We have meetings twice a month to discuss practical matters and group issues. We aim to make decision by consensus. We live relatively simply, by virtue of sharing resources, recycle some materials and eat a vegetarian diet. The cost of food is shared among us on a sliding scale according to income. We live in two groups, each sharing a kitchen. We eat together most evenings. Our accommodation is on three floors above what is now a leather shop in a building converted from old workshop spaces by founding members of the Community twenty or so years ago.

Status
existing community

Address
128 Bethnal Green Road
LONDON
E2 6DG

Telephone

Number of over 18s
14

Number of under 18s
0

Year started
1973

Situation
urban

Legal structure
Co Ltd by Shares

Open to new members?
Yes

We are a very mixed community of 14 living in two beautiful Victorian houses with a large garden, in a densely populated part of East London. We organise mainly through fortnightly meetings where consensus decisions are made. These are either "business meetings" (to discuss such issues as food, finances and repairs) or "get-togethers" (relationship meetings). Each household also has meetings to discuss the practicalities of day to day living. We have a unique rent system. We work out the community's expenditure and from this decide an average rent to cover costs. Each individual then decides how much they feel they can afford. If the total sum from everyone's rent is what we need *wonderful*, if not we enter into a process of negotiation. We have only once needed to do this. The ideological focus of the community is difficult to define. People are interested in ecology, therapy, the peace movement, films etc. We are gay and heterosexual and ages range from 25 to 51. There are also two lively young people of 13 and 16. Our "work" includes teaching peacework, therapy, and graphic design. We describe ourselves as a vegetarian community but some of us eat meat elsewhere.

MORNINGTON GROVE COMMUNITY

Status
existing community

Address
13-14 Mornington Grove
Bow
LONDON
E3 4NS

Telephone

Number of over 18s
12

Number of under 18s
2

Year started
1982

Situation
urban

Ideological focus
diverse

Legal structure
Ind & Prov Society

Open to new members?
Yes

FAMILY TREE COMMUNITY

Status
existing community

Address
*1 Queensdown Road
Hackney
LONDON
E5 8NN*

Telephone
0181 985 6908

Number of over 18s
8

Number of under 18s

Year started
1980

Situation
urban

Ideological focus
Christian

Legal structure
Registered Charity

Open to new members?
Yes

Family Tree is a small community of Christians and adults with moderate learning disabilities living and working together. We aim at enabling every member to live as normal a life as possible. This is achieved through sharing and support. We encourage individual empowerment quite positively and reasonable risk taking as well as responsibility, integration and informed choice. We also respect individuality and believe in the intrinsic and equal worth of each individual and their potential for personal development. The house has a relaxed homely and peaceful atmosphere in which all are treated equally. We all share in the household chores and hold weekly house meetings to inform and decide on future plans. There is a small management team which records, monitors and maintains the community covering areas such as complaints procedure, house rules, and equal opportunities to ensure every one's religious, racial and cultural values are taken into consideration, along with their gender, age, sexuality and ability. The essence of the community is corporate sharing; nevertheless we recognise that this may not be suitable for everyone or for every occasion. Therefore, the right to privacy and non-participation is respected. Family Tree is a registered charity with friendly co-operative members.

Wild Lavender was set up in Leeds in 1981 because a group of gay men wanted to create a supportive community as a counter to a society which isolates and discriminates against gay men. Since then there have been changes in location, membership and emphasis. At first it was a close knit 'therapeutic process' group that planned to move into the countryside, and some of its early members were responsible for setting up projects such as the Edward Carpenter Community and the Gay Men's Weeks at Laurieston Hall. Now its focus is less ideological - residents think of it primarily as their home. We are currently six gay men and a cat (Janet) who live in a large Victorian house in east London. We are non-smoking, vegetarian (meals are usually vegan), emphasise a holistic approach to life and aim to support each other. We run the house communally: chores and management tasks are shared; we have a cooking rota for the evening meal for whoever is in; and there is a weekly meeting which usually takes up an evening. Decisions are made consensually and we stress the importance of openly discussing interpersonal matters.

WILD LAVENDER

Status
existing community

Address
34 Queensdown Road
Hackney
LONDON
E5 8NN

Telephone
0181 533 0352

Electronic mail
pjohna@cix.compulink.
co.uk

Number of over 18s
6

Number of under 18s
0

Year started
1981

Situation
urban

Ideological focus
gay male

Legal structure
Ind & Prov Society

Open to new members?
Yes

THE GRAIL COMMUNITY

Status
existing community

Address
Waxwell Farm House
125 Waxwell Lane
PINNER
Middlesex
HA5 3ER

Telephone
0181 866 2195/0505

Fax
0181 866 1408

Number of over 18s
20 - 25

Number of under 18s
0

Year started
1932

Situation
edge of London

Ideological focus
Christian

Legal structure
Registered Charity

Open to new members?
Yes

The Grail Community is one of several branches of the Grail Society which was started in Holland in 1921. This is a Roman Catholic Institute of single and married people, men and women, both young and old. The society seeks, in an increasingly impersonal world, to promote understanding of the uniqueness and value of each person. The long term community, at 'Waxwell', Pinner, consists of women who, choosing to remain single, make a life commitment. Community life involves its members in a close interdependent relationship and life-style, sharing all resources and earnings and stressing each person's accountability to the community. The Grail carries the status of a registered charity. The community home, 'Waxwell' is an Elizabethan farmhouse with library, guest wing and conference extensions set in ten acres of cultivated and wilderness land. The work of the community includes: support for families and married people, publishing, hospitality, residential courses on arts, religion, human growth, focussing on the spiritual, helping those under stress, provision of space and solitude for those seeking rest and prayer. Short term members and volunteers are welcome. Short term members bring another dimension to community as they share our life for a year or so whilst exploring new directions. They participate fully in the life and work of the community.
Volunteers live along-side the community, assisting with the practical chores of the centre and the upkeep of the grounds. In addition to these there are regular participants in spinning and weaving classes, a healing group, prayer and Bible Study groups. People of all religious traditions are welcome.

The Community Creation Trust, founded and directed by Julie Lowe, is now established as a charity dedicated to environmental education, in building design and human behaviour generally. The Trust has been given a four-year lease of a 1.5 acre site behind Kings Cross Station, London, with buildings which include a long concrete barn.

COMMUNITY CREATION

Here the Battle Bridge Centre is coming to life. Timber chalets will be constructed to house 16 homeless people and to create within the barn a green village with a vegetarian restaurant, conservatory, resource centre, shops, offices, workshops and the RAJA Project, a holistic health service offering a wide range of therapies and including a detoxification programme. A large auditorium in the centre of the barn will be used for exhibitions, fairs and inter-faith events. A demonstration eco-house will be open to school children and other visitors. The development has started on site with the aid of volunteers and gifts of materials and cash.

The aim is to address specific local problems, which include homelessness, drug addiction, unemployment, and partially derelict locality; and to offer some services to a wider public via the eco-house and Raja. The Trust is also helping to set up a resource centre in Tamil Nadu, India. Offers of help or participation in any shape or form are welcome.

Status
existing community

Address
Battlebridge
LONDON
NW1 2TL

Telephone
0171 278 7172

Fax
0171 713 5657

Number of over 18s
8

Number of under 18s
0

Year started
1992

Situation
urban

Ideological focus
Ecological

Legal structure
Co Ltd by Guarantee

Open to new members?
Yes

GRAIGIAN SOCIETY

Status
existing community

Address
10 Lady Somerset Road
Kentish Town
LONDON
NW5 1UP

Telephone
0171 485 1646

Number of over 18s
4

Number of under 18s
0

Year started
1983

Situation
urban

Ideological focus
natural

Open to new members?
Yes

This is a monastic community with very strict rules - it is for men only. Submission to spiritual discipline and surrender to one's own real true feelings are an absolute necessity. The monks dress in striped, cotton habits of russet and green ... or in sage green and white striped tunics for casual wear. These are the only colours permitted. In North Wales, the monks own a tiny smallholding and cottage, Y Graig, where they spend some of their time. Most of their work is done at the Monastery in Kentish Town where they make pottery, produce books, paint, do calligraphy and frame pictures. The community wishes to establish a new religion based on Jungian principles. The Monastery aims to be the physical manifestation of the purified 'Inner'. The monks live out their own myth by means of dream-analysis and 'receiving'. They rise at 5.00am, have breakfast, do collective housework, building and repairs, then have 'Matins' (service) from 9am to 10am. After Matins the monks have lunch, a rest, then they all do their own individual work - besides being open to visitors interested in the work of the monastery. Decision making starts at breakfast and is based on 'receiving': a process of making feelings conscious. The approach to sexuality is the same and relates to what is usually unconscious. A great deal of attention is paid to a vegetarian diet and most food is cooked or baked in the monastery. The Green Monks buy their food wholesale, dip their own candles and ferment their own altar wine. Every fortnight there is a 'Sunday Group' for those interested in 'Natural Psychology'. On Moonday (Monday) elderberry wine and the Moonday Bread, made ritually from twelve ingredients, are shared. Interested people can ring between 2pm and 9pm ... or write (enclosing a sae). All income and all belongings are shared by the community, but there is a three month trial period for novices who will need to contribute between £30 and £50 a week including any money they earn at the monastery.

The Simon Community is a small registered charity working and living with homeless people. It aims to support those for whom no other provision exists and our philosophy is acceptance and tolerance. The Community operates an emergency night shelter and three residential houses as well as participating in extensive outreach work in the City of London. The Community is run on a group based structure: workers and residents sharing in the decision process. Volunteers are required throughout the year and should be nineteen or over, and looking to stay for six months or more; there are some shorter places available. Workers live in the project to which they are assigned; they receive full board and lodgings and a small weekly allowance as pocket money (£25). A workers house is available for days off. Every three months workers get two weeks leave and a substantial amount of money to ensure a good break. For long term workers there is a pattern of external training and internal training and support is provided for everyone throughout. Applicants attend a weekend following suitability for being a worker. Apply to the address given.

SIMON COMMUNITY

Status
existing community

Address
PO Box 1187
LONDON
NW5 4HW

Telephone
0171 485 6639

Number of over 18s
45

Number of under 18s
0

Year started
1963

Situation
urban

Ideological focus
none

Legal structure
Co Ltd by Guarantee &
Charity

Open to new members?
Yes

COMMUNITY OF ST PETER

In 1983 monks from Worth Abbey acquired St. Peters, a redundant church and vicarage as an ecumenical centre of prayer and an experiment in urban monasticism. In 1990 the monks withdrew and a group of lay people took over St. Peters as a lay community following a Benedictine lifestyle. The Community is both res-

Status
existing community

Address
522 Lordship Lane
East Dulwich
LONDON
SE22 8LD

Telephone

Number of over 18s
4

Number of under 18s
0

Year started
1990

Situation
urban

Ideological focus
Christian

Legal structure
Registered Charity

Open to new members?
Yes

idential and non-residential and has four key strands to its life - prayer, hospitality, ecumenism and community building. Since 1990 the community has grown and developed and put down strong roots supported by the local Anglican and Catholic dioceses. The site is still owned by Worth and the Community has it from Worth for one year at a time. Visitors are welcome but are expected to join in prayer and community meals and to make a financial contribution.

Founded by Emily Ayckbowm in 1870, the Community of the Sisters of the Church is an international body of women within the Anglican Communion, living under the gospel values of Poverty, Chastity and Obedience, desiring to be faithful to the traditions of the Religious Life while exploring new ways of expressing them and of living community life and ministry today. Our worship as a Community in the fourfold Divine Office and the Eucharist, together with our personal prayer, form the centre of our daily life. We experiment with liturgy and try to be inclusive both in language and imagery about God and humanity. Creative activities enable growth and wholeness for vital living. These include: candle making, painting, pottery, card making, music, gardening, cooking, writing,.... Sisters are engaged in a variety of pastoral ministries within and beyond the institutional church. By our worship and life in community, we want to enable others to encounter the living God whom we seek, desiring to be channels of the reconciling love and acceptance of Christ, while acknowledging the dignity of every human person. Community Houses are located in Australia, Canada, England and the Solomon Islands.

COMMUNITY OF SISTERS OF THE CHURCH

Status
existing community

Address
St Michael's Convent
56 Ham Common
RICHMOND
Surrey
TW10 7JH

Telephone
0181 940 8711

Fax
0181 332 2927

Number of over 18s
16 at mother house

Number of under 18s
0

Year started
1870

Situation
suburban

Ideological focus
Christian

Legal structure
Registered Charity

Open to new members?
Yes

HOUSING CO-OPS IN GREATER LONDON

EAST LONDON

Mile End Housing Co-op
68 Bromley Street E1 0NB.
Belgrave Street Housing Co-op
49 Belgrave Street E1 0NG.
•**East Stepney Housing Co-op**
30 Westport Street E1 0RA.
Sylhet Housing Co-op *28 Myrdle Street E1 1EU. 0171 401 3131.*
Mitali Housing Co-op
First Floor, 18 New Road E1 2AX.
•**Adelina Housing Co-op** *1-3 Grove Dwellings, Adelina Grove E1 3AE. 0171 790 5503. 100 Ad, 60 Ch.*
Dallo Housing Co-op *Dame Colet House, Ben Jonson Road E1 3NH.*
La Caye Housing Co-op *Room 12, Wickham House, 10 Cleveland Way E1 4TR.*
•**Karin Housing Co-op** *Room 26, Wickham House, 10 Cleveland Way E1 4TZ. 0171 790 7572.*
•**Spitalfields Co-op Housing Association**
172 Brick Lane, Spitalfields E1 6RU.
•**Shahazalal Housing Co-op** *Stepney Meeting House, 147 Stepney Way E1.*
•**Leytonstone Housing Co-op**
57a Whipps Cross Road E11 1NS. 0181 989 0697. 25 Ad, 10 Ch.
•**Hashem Housing Co-op**
43 Coleville Road, Leyton E11.
•**July 14 Housing Co-op**
Greater London House, 541-551 Leytonstone High Road E11.
Woodgrange Park Village Co-op *c/o Community Centre, Bluebell Av E12 8UL. 0181 503 5041. 150 Ad.*
Glenkerry Co-op Housing Ass Ltd *The Office, Glenkerry House, Burcham Street E14 0SL. 0171 515 8645.*
•**Labo Housing Co-op** *Suites 1 & 2, Dormers Court, Thomas Rd E14 7BJ.*

•**Birchfield Housing Co-op**
1 Birchfield House, Birchfield Street E14 8EY.
Clays Lane Housing Co-op
Community Centre, Clays Lane, Stratford E15 2HJ.
Ad Hoc Housing Co-op *27 Ad, 8 Ch.*
Banyan Housing Co-op
Box Housing Co-op *20 Ad, 5 Ch.*
New Hampsters Housing Co-op *20 Ad, 5 Ch.*
Newham Short Life Housing *35 Ad, 10 Ch.*
Our New Housing Co-op
Rush Housing Co-op *15 Ad, 5 Ch.*
•**X-Rayz Associates** *40 Ad.*
all care of
Newham Community Housing, Suite 7, Essex House, 375-377 High Street E15 4OZ.
Permanent Housing Co-op
81 Cedars Road, Stratford E15 4OZ.
Home From Home Housing Co-op *Suite 2, Essex House, 375 High St E15 4QZ.*
•**Longlife Housing Co-op** *Suite 6, Essex House, 375-377 High St E15 4QZ. 0181 519 9708. 82 Ad.*
Phoenix Community Housing Co-op
119 Roman Road, Bethnal Green E2 0QN.
Grand Union Housing Co-op
101b Bishops Way E2 9HL.
•**TUSH Housing Co-op**
48 Bruce Road E3 3HL.
•**Dennis Central London Housing Co-op**
29 Bracken House, Watts Grove E3 3RG. 0171 987 3834. 100 Ad, 25 Ch.
•**Everbrook Housing Co-op**
117 Rendlesham Road E5 8PA.
•**Hackney Housing Co-op**
117 Rendlesham Road E5 8PA.
Winsor Housing Co-op
6 Winsor Terrace E6 4LE.

Newham Tamil Housing Co-op
18 Grosvenor Road E7.
•**HCH2 Housing Co-op**
85 Kingsland High Street E8 2PB.
•**October Housing Co-op**
85 Kingsland High Street E8 2PB.
•**Mace Housing Co-op**
*The Print House, 18 Ashwin Street
E8 3DL. 0171 254 9560. 200 Ad.*
•**Mapledene Housing Co-op** *47 Wilton
Way E8 3ED. 0171 275 9225.*
London Fields Housing Co-op
118 Albion Drive E8 4LY.
Lansdowne Women's Co-op
176 Lansdowne Drive E8 4NE.
Bricks For Women Housing Co-op
*c/o Women's Link, 1a Snow Hill
Court EC1A 2EJ. 0171 248 1600.*
SUPPORT ORGANISATIONS
Solon CHS (East) *148 Cambridge Heath
Road E1 5QJ. 0171 702 7350.*
Newham Community Housing
*Suite 7, Essex House,
375-377 High Street E15 4OZ.*

NORTH LONDON

New Roof Housing Co-op *18 Elmore
Street N1 3AL. 0171 704 8119. 14 Ad.*
Samouar Housing Co-op
42 Halliford Street N1 3EL. 8 Ad.
South Mildmay Housing Co-op
*52 Mildmay Park N1 4PR.
0171 249 8280. 130 Ad.*
•**April Housing Co-op** *Unit A15, Metro-
politan Workshops, Enfield Road
N1 5AZ. 0171 254 9560. 12 Ad, 3 Ch.*
Shepherdess Walk Housing Co-op
*103 Shepherdess Walk N1 7QD.
0171 474 7084. 32 Ad, 12 Ch.*
Tally Ho Housing Co-op
*3a Moss Hall Crescent, North
Finchley N12 8NY. 0181 445 0560.*
Clissold Housing Co-op
5 Clissold Road N16 9EX.
Seaview Housing Co-op *108 Ranelagh*

Road, Tottenham N17 6XT.
Ladybur Housing Co-op *68 Ladysmith Rd
N17 9AG. 0181 801 6700. 211 Ad, 60 Ch.*
Temple Housing Co-op *13 Hale Road,
Tottenham N17 9LB. 15 Ad, 3 Ch.*
Brooke-Park Tenants Co-op *48 Schole-
field Road, Hornsey Rise Estate
N19 3DH. 0171 272 4457. 115 Ad.*
Hornsey Lane Estate Management Ass
*Board Embay House, Hornsey Lane
Estate N19 3YJ. 0171 272 7977.*
William Allen Housing Co-op
*4 Mercers Road, Highbury N19 4PJ.
0171 281 0650. 40 Ad, 4 Ch.*
Waverley (8th) Co-op
*19a Shaftesbury Road N19 4QW.
0171 263 3536. 35 Ad, 12 Ch.*
St Pancras Court Housing Co-op
*52a St Pancras Court, High Road,
East Finchley N2 9AE. 0181 444
2100. 140 Ad, 25 Ch.*
N17 Housing Co-op *14 Beechfield Road
N4 1PE. 0181 800 8123. 20 Ad.*
Alamo Housing Co-op *43 Hanley Road
N4 3DY. 0171 272 3391. 550 Ad, 40 Ch.*
Stroud Green Housing Co-op
*Unit 1, Albert Mews, Albert Road
N4 3RD. 0171 263 2716. 71 Ad.*
New Swift Housing Co-op
12 Pine Grove N4.
Harecourt Community Housing Ass *63 Pyr-
land Road, Highbury N5 2JA. 9 Ad.*
Quadrant Brownswood Tenant Co-op
*43 - 45 Mountgrove Road N5 2LX.
0171 359 9360. 160 Ad.*
Black Sheep Housing Co-op
*103 Grosvenor Avenue N5 2NL.
0171 226 2951. 18 Ad.*
•**Habbarfield Housing Co-op** *15 Nelson
Road N8 9RX. 12 Ad, 4 Ch.*

NORTH WEST LONDON

Georgiana Street Housing Co-op
*31 Georgiana Street NW1 0EB.
0171 482 5023. 42 Ad, 2 Ch.*

Carol Street Housing Co-op *2 Carol street NW1 0HU. 0171 482 3668. 70 Ad.*
Camden People's Housing Co-op *2 Carol St NW1 0HU. 0171 267 8302. 24 Ad.*
Claddagh Housing Co-op *12 Greenland Street, Camden Town NW1 0LU.*
Infil Housing Co-op
51 Chalcot Road NW1 8LY.
0171 722 9994. 320 Ad, 30 Ch.
Castle Road Housing Co-op
30 Castle Road NW1 8PP. 2 Ad.
South Camden Housing Co-op
16c Stratford Villas, Camden Town NW1 9SG. 30 Ad, 5 Ch.
Cyron Housing Co-op *6 Bridge House, Chamerlayne Road NW10 3NR.*
0181 964 5700. 70 Ad.
Abeona Housing Co-op *24 Fleet Road NW3 2QS. 0171 482 2138. 50 Ad, 7 Ch.*
Camden Teachers' Tenants' Co-op
2-4 Ospringe Road NW5 2JE.
0171 485 7378. 16 Ad, 6 Ch.
Tenants Association of North Camden Co-op
First Floor, 106 Malden Road NW5 4DA. 0171 267 7118.
•Kilburn Vale Housing Co-op *Sycamore Hall, West End Lane, (next to 27) NW6 1QJ. 0171 370. 410 Ad.*
West Hampstead Housing Co-op *82 Kingsgate Road, Kilburn NW6 4LA.*
0171 328 8756. 200 Ad.
Kilburn Housing Co-op Ltd
67c Willesden Lane NW6 7RL.
Kilburn Square Housing Co-op *Kilburn Square, Victoria Road NW6.*

WEST LONDON

Richmond Co-op Housing Association
58 Queens Road, Twickenham, Middlesex TW1 4EX. 30 Ad.
W11 Housing Co-op
16 Lancaster Road W11 1QR. 0171 727 8763. 50 Ad, 10 Ch.
•Bramleys Housing Co-op
4a Willow Way W11 4BS.

W14 Housing Co-op *Highmasters House, 153 Hammersmith Road W14 0QL. 0181 563 2602. 70 Ad, 2 Ch.*
The Bridge Housing Co-op *80 Elsham Rd W14 8HH. 0171 603 4140. 8 Ad.*
•Seymour Housing Co-op *20a Seymour Buildings, Seymour Place W1H 5TQ. 0171 723 3203. 90 Ad, 10 Ch.*
Dawley Housing Co-op
Green Brick Housing Co-op
Green Park Housing Co-op
Hogarth Housing Co-op
Middlesex Housing Association
Middlesex Housing Co-op
Watermans Housing Co-op
Wellington Housing Co-op
Zin Zan Housing Co-op
all care of
Co-operative Home Services,
367 Chiswick High Road W4 4AG.
Ealing Housing Co-op *62 Hangar Lane, Ealing W5. 0181 991 0316. 50 Ad, 4 Ch.*
Chippenham Co-op H.A. *27 Chippenham Road W9 2AH. 17 Ad, 10 Ch.*
SUPPORT ORGANISATION
Co-operative Home Services
367 Chiswick High Road W4 4AG.

SOUTH EAST LONDON

La Gaitana Housing Co-op *Room 7, 2nd Floor, Docklands Enterprise Centre, 11 Marshalsea Road SE1 1EP.*
Arundel Buildings Housing Co-op
17 Arundel Buildings, Webb Street SE1 4RZ.
Brighton Buildings Housing Co-op
62 Tower Bridge Road SE1 4TR.
Wellington Mills Tenant Co-op *24 Mead Row SE1 7JG. 0171 633 0255.*
New Cut Housing Co-op
106 The Cut SE1 8LN.
0171 401 3131.
Alexandra Housing Co-op
Allnutt Mill Housing Co-op
Anerley Housing Co-op

Atwell Housing Co-op
Baltic Housing Co-op
Barnwood Housing Co-op
Belpark One Housing Co-op
Blackwood Co-op Housing Society
Bonham & Strathleven Tenants Co-op
Colyers Housing Co-op
Craymill Housing Co-op
Darent Housing Co-op
Delce Manor Housinig Co-op
Ekarro Housing Co-op
Elles Housing Co-op
Fairfield Co-op Housing Society
Franklyn Housing Co-op
Gads Hill Housing Co-op
Greendale Co-op Housing Society
Halcyon Co-op Housing Society
Hatherley Housing Co-op
Hazel Housing Co-op
Hillbury Road Residents Co-op
Lewisham Family Co-op Association
Lindsey Housing Co-op
Mayday Permanent Housing Co-op
Moat Farm Housing Co-op
Normandy Housing Co-op
Oast Wood Housing Co-op
Perryview Housing Co-op
Phoenix Co-op Housing Society
Pine Tree Housing Co-op
Riverdale Housing Co-op
Senacre Housing Co-op
Shearwood Housing Co-op
Shorncliffe Housing Co-op
Southward Housing Co-op
St Georges Church Housing Co-op
Swan Lane Housing Co-op
Temeraire Housing Co-op
Townshend Close Housing Co-op
Warwick Housing Co-op
Weybank Housing Co-op
Whitworth Housing Co-op
Mulberry Housing Co-op
(some of these co-ops will be out-side Greater London)

all care of CDS, 207 Waterloo Road SE1 8XW. 0171 401 3131.
Edward Henry Housing Co-op
23 Edward Henry House, Cornwall Road SE1 8YE. 86 Ad.
Palm Housing Co-op
Redwood Housing Co-op *120 Ad.*
•Fred Miller Housing Co-op
•Iroko Housing Co-op
•Lime Housing Co-op
•Mangrove Housing Co-op
all care of CSS, 99 Upper Ground SE1 9PP. 0171 620 0544.
South London Arts Housing Co-op
11 Kennington Park Place SE11 4AS.
St Agnes Place Housing Co-op *60 St Agnes Place, Kennington SE11 4PE.*
South Bank Housing Co-op Ltd *24 Hayles Street, Kennington SE11 4SU.*
St Oswald's Place Housing Co-op
28 St Oswald's Pl SE11 5JE.
6 Ad, 1 Ch.
Oval Mansions Housing Co-op *38 Oval Mansions, Kennington Oval SE11. 0171 582 3940. 60 Ad, 4 Ch.*
New Venture Housing Co-op
Flat 11, Venture Court, 3 Horncastle Road SE12 9LH.
Red Stripe Housing Co-op
49b Micheldever Road SE12.
SE13 Housing Co-op
63 Sandrock Road SE13 7TX.
Tardis Housing Co-op *13 Pankhurst Cl, Briant Street SE14 5HW. 22 Ad.*
Flamenco Housing Co-op *19 Waller Rd, New Cross SE14 5LE.*
Able Housing Alliance *4 Billington Road, New Cross SE14 5QQ. 0181 691 5534. 9 Ad.*
Greenstreet Housing Co-op *77 Drakefell Road, Lewisham SE14 5SH.*
Towering Housing Co-op *24 Nettleton Road, New Cross SE14 5UJ.*
Nettleton Road Housing Co-op *8 Nettleton Road, New Cross SE14 5UJ. 4 Ad.*

Fusions Jameen Self-Build Housing Co-op
21 Marchant Street, New Cross
SE14 6HP.
Sanford Housing Co-op
11 Sanford Walk, New Cross
SE14 6NB. 0181 692 7316. 130 Ad.
Blue Moon Housing Co-op
36 Bird In Bush Road SE15. 3 Ad.
Mayday Housing Co-op
72 Kingsgrove, Peckham SE15 2NB.
Argoth Housing Co-op
17b Lyndhurst Grove SE15 5AN.
Sharsted Self-Build Association
109 Crabtree Walk, Camden Estate,
Peckham SE15 5PE.
Bash Street Housing Co-op
15 Sears Street SE15 7JI.
Southwark Park Housing Co-op *389-391*
Southwark Park Road SE16 2JH.
Housing Co-op in the Blue
163 Abbeyfield Road SE16.
0171 237 0197. 18 Ad, 6 Ch.
Browning Estate Management Ass *31*
Tennyson House, Browning Street
SE17 1DE. 0171 708 0708. 430 Ad.
Balfour Street Housing Co-op
73b Balfour Street SE17 1PL.
Kaleidoscope Housing Co-op *156*
Lakedale Rd, Plumstead SE18 1PS.
The Hill Housing Co-op *11 Edge Hill*
SE18 3SQ.
Greenwich Self-Build Housing Co-op
3c Llanover Rd, Woolwich SE18 3ST.
Off-Cut Housing Co-op *62b Alexandra*
Drive, Gypsy Hill SE19 1AN.
Gypsy Hill Housing Co-op *21 Farquhar*
Road, Norwood SE19 1SS.
0181 244 5984. 40 Ad, 10 Ch.
Ewart Road Housing Co-op *44 Wastdale*
Rd SE23 1HW. 0181 699 6074. 400 Ad.
Front Line Housing Co-op
1b St George's Residences,
78-80 Railton Road SE24 0LG.
Alder Housing Co-op *15 Venner Road,*

Sydenham SE26 5EQ.
Kirkdale Housing Co-op *87/95 Lawrie*
Park Grdns SE26 6HW. 0171 401 3131.
Sydenham Housing Co-op
73 Kent House Road, Sydenham
SE26. 0181 776 8212. 25 Ad, 24 Ch.
West Norwood Housing Co-op
100 Thornlaw Road SE27 0SB.
Brockley Tenants Housing Co-op
249 Lewisham Way SE4 1XF.
Tressillian Housing Co-op
182b Tressillian Road SE4 1XY.
0181 694 9957. 13 Ad, 18 Ch.
Three Boroughs Housing Co-op
188a Brockley Road, Brockley
SE4 2BN. 0181 469 3690.
Lewisham Family Self Help Housing
Association *188a Brockley Road,*
Brockley SE4 2RN. 0181 692 9294.
CHISEL Housing Association
188a Brockley Road SE4 2RN.
0181 694 1840. 68 Ad.
Kikombe Housing Co-op *8 Urlwin Street,*
Camberwell SE5 0NF.
Walworth Road Housing Co-op *14 Urlwin*
Street, Camberwell SE5 0NF.
Matrix Housing Co-op
4 Oswyth Road SE5 8NH.
Camberwell Grove Housing Co-op
208 Camberwell Grove SE5 8RJ.
Excalibur Tenant Management Co-op
1 Baudwin Road, Catford SE6 1RN.
0181 461 5768. 170 Ad.
Latin American Women's Housing Co-op
1d Catford Broadway, Catford
SE6 4SP. 0181 690 8120.
Oxleas Housing Co-op *11 Floyd Road,*
Charlton SE7 8AY.
Crusaders Housing Co-op
80 Carteret Way, Pepys Estate SE8.
0181 694 2394. 150 Ad, 12 Ch.
Lamerton Street Housing Co-op
13 Lamerton St, Deptford SE8 3PL.
Deptford Housing Co-op *The Community*

Centre, 16 Rochdale Way SE8 4LY.
0181 692 4141. 120 Ad, 10 Ch.
May Day (Short Life) Housing Co-op 136a
Evelyn Street, Deptford SE8 5DD.
Middlemarch Housing Co-op 132b Evelyn
Street, Deptford SE8 5DD.
Bromley Housing Co-op c/o 52 Ravens-
croft Rd, Beckenham, Kent
BR3 4TR. 0181 289 5301.
SUPPORT ORGANISATIONS
CDS Co-op Housing Society Ltd
207 Waterloo Road SE1 8XW.
0171 461 3131.
Coin Street Secondary Housing Co-op
99 Upper Ground SE1 9PP.
0171 620 0544.
Southwark Federation of Shortlife Users
24 Hayles Street SE11.
South London Family Housing Association,
Co-ops Unit Rochester House,
2-10 Belvedere Road SE19 2HL.
0181 768 0890.
Hexagon Housing Association
Co-ops & Tenant Services Team,
139-141 Sydenham Road,
Sydenham SE26 5HJ.
0181 778 6699.

SOUTH WEST LONDON

Home Comfort Housing Co-op 45c Crusoe
Road, Mitcham, Surrey, CR4 3LG.
0181 646 5550.
Croydon Short Life Users Group
353 Bensham Lane,
Thornton Heath, Croydon CR7 7ER.
Goulden House Co-op 140 Goulden
House, Winders Rd SW11 3HF. 120 Ad.
Solon Wandsworth Housing Association
49a Lavender Hill SW11 5QN.
0171 223 7376.
Gateway Housing Co-op
155 Battersea Rise SW11. 25 Ad.
New World Housing Asso 8 Grange Mills,
Weir Road, Balham SW12 0NE.
0181 675 0320.

Wandsworth Community Housing Co-op
51 Oldridge Rd SW12 8PP.
•**Felsham Road Co-op** 87 Felsham Road,
Putney SW15 1BA.
Skylight Housing Co-operative
43a The Broadway SW19 1QD.
Wimbledon Park Co-op 2 Fernwood,
Albert Drive SW19 6LR.
0181 780 9980. 200 Ad.
No 1 Housing Co-op 1 St Matthews Rd,
Brixton SW2 1ND.
Streatham Housing Co-op
48 Craster Road SW2 2AU.
Flying Buttress Housing Co-op
58 Larkhall Lane SW4 6SP.
Short Stock Housing Co-op
121 Park Hill SW4 9NX.
Park Hill Housing Co-op 13 Allard
Gardens, Briarwood Rd SW4 9QA.
Vine Housing Co-op 17 Vauxhall Grove
SW8 1SY. 0171 793 7564. 70 Ad.
High Priority Housing Co-op 105 Lans-
downe Way, Stockwell SW8 2PB.
Black Roof Housing Co-op 21a Groveway
SW9 0AH. 0171 924 0960. 38 Ad, 14 Ch.
Hourglass Housing Co-op 71 Clapham Rd
SW9 0HY. 0171 735 2384. 15 Ad, 4 Ch.
Villa Road Housing Co-op
21 Villa Road, Brixton SW9 7ND.
Clapham Rise Housing Co-op
359 Clapham Rd SW9 9BT. 12 Ad.
Coronation Housing Co-op
72 Hubert Grove SW9 9NY.
Avalon Housing Co-op
32 Dalyell Road SW9 9QR.
Sphinx Housing Co-op
3 Chantrey Road SW9 9TD.
•**Carlton Mansions Housing Co-op**
2 Carlton Mansions,
387 Coldharbour Lane SW9. 16 Ad.
SUPPORT ORGANISATION
Lambeth Federation of Housing Co-ops
260 Coldharbour Lane SW9 8SE.
0171 733 7370.

A COMMUNITY PROJECT

Status

embryonic community

Address

care of
72 Lowden Road
LONDON
SE24 0BH

Telephone

0171 737 4403 or 272 2371

Fax

0171 326 4961

Intended Situation

rural

Ideological focus

We are proposing to gather together a group of people in order to purchase jointly a large country property with enough land for extensive gardens and even a small farming operation for those interested. We would need to set up a housing association/ co-operative. The property would then be divided into self-contained units (flats or cottages) bought leasehold from the co-op, whose members would jointly manage the shared parts, ie the grounds and gardens, communal rooms (eg laundry facilities) etc and share the freehold. We are convinced that living in a community can enable us to achieve the apparent paradox of living more cheaply and to have a better quality of life. Co-operatively buying a large property gives access to a kind of housing and grounds otherwise available only to the very rich. At the same time, this way of living should help us to live more sustainably.

CONNECTIONS

Status

embryonic community

Address

care of The Old School
Rudland
Kirbymoorside, YORK
YO6 6JJ

Telephone

01751 431144

Intended Situation

rural but accessible

Ideological focus

Spiritual

A small nucleus is growing but is, as yet, unstructured. We are seeking an opportunity to live with others where ... we will connect ... with ourselves (through personal growth work) ... with others (through community living) ... with nature, seen and unseen (in our organic gardens, woods and meadows) ... with the Universe (through our meditation and healing work) A central building offering day and evening "events" - will gradually be surrounded by ecologically sound self-build homes. Thus balancing needs for individuality, with a desire for sharing. We will give what we have to offer to our joint venture - and will receive what we need in return. Our community will be alive, evolving and increasingly self sustaining - but with contact, through choice, with the outside world. Through creativity and commitment we will aim to hold a healing space, offering love, harmony and joy to ourselves and others. we will acknowledge the oneness of all.

HOME

Status
embryonic community

Address
care of Diggers & Dreamers

Telephone

Intended Situation
rural (with urban connections)

Ideological focus
Holistic

Are you interested in pursuing a holistic life-style? Are you considering where to go from here?

We are a group of eight adults and four children, who have in mind an art/music/therapy/spiritual workshop kind of community or co-operative of perhaps 20 to 30 adults ... to be both self-sufficient yet effectively connected to the world outside.

We envisage a way of life that is moulded and shaped by the group to more fully express our lives as individuals; that encourages whole-hearted enthusiasm to create results quite unlikely to be achieved as isolated nuclear families or as single people.

We welcome enquiries from potentially serious companions. We have formulated a fairly comprehensive questionnaire which should help both you and present members of our group to decide whether we could enjoy working together towards a possible partnership.

LIVING GREEN

Status
embryonic community

Address
care of 28 Pancras Road
LONDON
NW1 2TB

Telephone
0171 837 1661

Fax
0171 837 1661

Intended Situation
rural

Ideological focus
Spiritual

We are a group of people who have been meeting regularly in central London for three years to plan the development of a spiritually focused, environmentally sustainable village. Legally we are both a registered Housing Co-operative (Gometra Housing Co-op) and a registered educational charity - the Living Green Trust. We have a core group of around 12 members who are working together developing our urban centre. We hold regular member meetings, and run workshops, courses and a Volunteer Programme for young people interested in helping with the research and development of the village. We aim to buy land in a rural area and develop accommodation for a residential group of between 100 and 150 people. The land itself will be co-operatively owned and managed by Gometra, but each individual or family will be given a lease on their own private accommodation garden. The group holds Open Days on the first Saturday of every month.

PROMETHEUS PROJECT COMMUNITY

Status

embryonic community

Address

31 Caerau Road
Caerau, Maesteg
BRIDGEND, Mid Glamorgan
CF34 0PB

Telephone

01656 739813

Intended Situation

urban

Ideological focus

eco-developmental

Phase one includes the running of free shops in Caerau and Maesteg and talking via the Internet to interest users in creating technological, ecological communities of an advanced design; phase two being the building of such communities, after the startup capital is acquired. Only non-smokers need apply to join. It is hoped that the communities of phase two will decide, democratically, to be non-smoking. There is more chance of this if we make it a requirement of the promoters. Creative eccentrics welcome, followers who need leading not so welcome but will be considered on merit. There is a newly grant-renovated four bedroom house for accommodation. Children acceptable, pets not. This is a community that intends to make a paying business out of making the world a better place. We are not simply trying to make a point or a gesture, we are trying to make a difference.

CENTRE FOR SUSTAINABLE LIVING

Status

embryonic community

Address

care of 1 Russell Avenue
AYLESBURY
Buckinghamshire
HP21 8NE

Telephone

01296 436129

Intended Situation

rural

Ideological focus

sustainability

The idea of the Centre is to explore the practicalities of sustainable living, and to actively promote a sustainable lifestyle for all. The community would be loose-knit, "living apart together", and balanced between looking inward and outward: the former to ensure health and viability; the latter for vitality and stimulation (in both directions). Its location similarly balances the need for land and an attractive environment with proximity to centres of population and local facilities. Sustainable living? It means being partially self-sufficient; welcoming diversity and respecting diverse views; being willing to learn and understand the full consequences of our actions and inactions and using this awareness to guide every decision. Actively promote? As well as setting an example, things like encouraging visitors; workshops; involving the wider community; liaising with schools and colleges; individuals campaigning with the support of the group.

ASHRAM COMMUNITY TRUST

Status

network

Address

178 Abbeyfield Road
SHEFFIELD
S4 7AY

Telephone

0114 243 6688

Ashram Community exists to support members, ministries, people and projects. Our organisation is minimal but serves to keep us responsible to each other and to our aims and vision. Ashram Community is a group of about 80 people, spread around Britain. We meet twice yearly as a whole community and in smaller groups more frequently, to create and sustain the community's life and its implications for individual members. We support each other in discipleship to the radical Jesus, today. This expresses itself in various ways such as practical gospel study, seeking calls that are relevant today and helping each other with the hard decisions they lead to. We do not insist on consensus but search for appropriate ways to change our lifestyles to take account of a divided world. We are of all ages and have overseas members. A joyful community of simple liturgies, sharing and challenging each other.

CONFEDERATION OF CO-OPERATIVE HOUSING

Status

network

Address

care of Diggers & Dreamers

Telephone

01908 314685

There are over 3000 housing co-operatives in England and Wales and CCH is working towards representing them in every aspect. It aims to make housing co-ops a form of housing recognised by the public at large and official bodies. Housing co-operatives are an effective form of housing situated between the private sector and social housing, with real tenant control and the very important aspect of creating communities. CCH is represented on the UK Co-operative Council and has places on the standing committee feeding into the All Party Parliamentary Group on Housing Co-ops. It was formed two years ago when many people in the co-op movement thought that there must be representation at a national level to defend the rights of tenants/ members and promote the formation of housing co-ops throughout the UK. It is a purely voluntary body with representation from local federations and individual co-ops. Effort has been made to avoid it being London orientated - meetings are held all over the country. With no central office CCH depends on the facilities of the members and their feds of co-ops. Further membership is sought from groups and individual housing co-ops - the more the better!

THE FAMILY

Status

network

Address

BM Box 8440
LONDON
WC1N 3XX

Telephone

01455 209172

Fax

01455 202073

We have a very structured life in our communities, and after 27 years of experimenting with communal living those who have visited our communities often comment on how we are the most organised communal group they have seen. The daily schedule usually consists of all adults coming together for a short devotional reading after breakfast and then breaking up to go to their respective duties. Once a week there is a counsel meeting where all those aged 16 and up attend to make united decisions on policies pertaining to the individual commune. The main body that oversees the running of one of our communities is called a Teamwork and consists of at least three members who manifest leadership qualities in the areas of caring for people, business, teaching and child care abilities, and general home care. The Teamwork is chosen by democratic vote by the Home members. We have found that a good balance is kept in the running of the house. Decisions that involve the whole community are made in the weekly Home meeting.

LEE ABBEY HOUSEHOLD COMMUNITIES

Status

network

Address

care of
14 Gorway Gardens
WALSALL
West Midlands
WS1 3BJ

Telephone

01922 26010

Fax

01922 25924

There are currently three Lee Abbey Household Communities which are part of the Lee Abbey Fellowship - with larger communities in Devon and London. The three households are in Birmingham, Bristol and Walsall. Members are either in paid employment or work voluntarily in the local area. The community life is based on daily prayer, shared finances and eating together. Members seek to live out the Christian faith in daily living.

NEW CREATION CHRISTIAN COMMUNITY

Status

network

Address

*New Creation Farmhouse
Nether Heyford, NORTHAMPTON
NN7 3LB*

Telephone

01327 349991

Fax

01327 349997

Electronic mail

jesusa@dircon.co.uk

NCCC consists of 60-plus households in various locations, principally in Central England. The Community is a part of the Jesus Fellowship Church, well-known to many for its Jesus Army gospel outreach activity. Theologically we're Reformed, Evangelical and Charismatic and support all the historic Christian creeds and doctrines. Our all-things-in-common lifestyle gains inspiration from the Christians in Jerusalem in the first days of the Church. All of us have experienced the life-changing power of God through faith in Jesus, and we want to live out this new life in a new way that shows the love and life of God. Backgrounds vary; some are (very) rough, others more respectable. As long as you are in sympathy with our aims and willing to participate in our daily activities and worship, you're welcome. Hospitality is freely provided for short stays, and there is a low charge made for longer visits, though we won't turn you away just because you can't pay!

RADICAL ROUTES

Status

network

Address

*42 South Road
Hockley
BIRMINGHAM
B18 5NB*

Telephone

0121 551 1679

Radical Routes is a network of independent co-operatives working fo social change. We are creating bases from which to resist and challenge dominant structures in society and aim to develop an alternative economy and way of living. Through close co-operation we are taking control over property and land, developing economic and educational ventures and community based projects, all with the aim of empowering people at grassroots level. Radical Routes co-ordinates and provides a focus for its member co-operatives. These groups determine Radical Routes policies and control its actions. It also raises money for co-operative development. To this end it operates an ethical investment scheme which raises large amounts of money from sympathetic organisations and like minded individuals. This fund enables member co-operatives to borrow money they could not otherwise raise at rates well below commercial levels. In this way the network is consolidated and extended.

Overseas

This listing represents a sample of intentional communities around the world. In this edition we have listed only those communities who replied to our mailing in spring 1995, so you can be reasonably sure that the information is up-to-date. We have made no attempt to cover North America. The latest edition of *Communities Directory*, produced by the Federation of Intentional Communities in the States, lists 550 groups there, and has an international list which includes communities not listed below. See advert on page 224. They also have a web site on the Internet (http://www.well.com/www/cmty) which promises to be very interesting. Other good sources of information on communities worldwide are scattered through the following pages. Our thanks go to them for their good research and co-operation. When planning to visit any of these groups, please remember that they are people's homes. Write to them first, and wait for them to invite you. It is a courtesy to include an International Reply Coupon. Telephone numbers include the usual international prefix. Any prefix needed from within the country is given in brackets.

EUROPE

AUSTRIA

Mag. Friedrich Köstlinger A-3710 Frauendorf 76. *This community has sent a list of communities in Austria, which we can send you for private use (stamped envelope please). If you want to let your life be blessed by the LOVE which created this world, and feel you should do this in a community in Austria, do contact Mag. Friedrich Köstlinger.*

Sonnenhof Ritterkamp 7, A-3911 Rappottenstein. ✆ 0043 (0)2828 264 *Founded 1987; small international community. Making safe learning environment for the adventurous exploration of group consciousness, and using this group energy to serve others. Central theme is unconditional love, and guidance from the higher self. Ecological co-operative lifestyle.*

BELGIUM

Colline de Penuel 192 chemin de Vieusart, B-1300 Wavre *Christian: prolonged solitary prayer.*

Communauté Dominicaine de Froidmont Ferme de Froidmont, B-1330 Rixensart. ✆ 0032 (0)2 655 0094 Fax 655 0102 *Christian: lay / religious; only some living together.*

Foyers Communautaires Shalom - La Moisson place de l'Eglise 15, B-6962 Houmont. *Aim: to reinstate people with a social handicap. We offer: psycho-social and administrative help. Our fulfilment: forest work; cattle breeding; gardening; producing of organic fertiliser and flower worms (for fishing); timber work.*

Communauté de la Poudrière rue de la Poudrière 60, B-1000 Bruxelles. ✆ 0032 (0)2 512 90 22 Fax (0)2 512 32 86 *90 adults and 17 children living in five centres in Belgium (Brussels, Anderlecht, Vilvoorde, Rummen & Péruwelz). Pluralist: open in principle to all philosophies and religions; accent is laid on working together. Begun in 1958.*

Communauté de la Vieille Voie Vieille Voie de Tongres 33, B-4000 Liège. ✆ 0032 (0)41 266077 Fax (0)41 267670 *11 adults, 16 children. The community is also called* *"habitat groupé de Sainte-Walburge"* because it is formed by 6 houses built near each other. Life is moderately communal: we share the garden, we have a common meeting room, a room to host visitors and a small chapel. We also share a meal per week, we hold regular meetings and we have daily common prayer. We are all Christians closely linked to the life of the parish and area of Sainte-Walburge.

CZECH REPUBLIC

Ladronka Autonomie, POB 223, 111 21 Praha 1. ℂ 0042 2 541867 (Lenka Pechalová) *Best known Prague squat. Plans submitted for use of building as an Autonomous Social Cultural Centre, but eviction notices served. They request petitions, letters of solidarity and/or donations to mailing address given. Squat at Tomanova 1, Praha 6 - Brevnov. Black flag over door.*

DENMARK

KoKoo Rådhusstræde 13, DK-1466 København K. *The Danish Communes Association is winding up. But it is still possible to get information about communities and visitors conditions by writing to the address.*

National Association for Sustainable Communities (Landsforenigen for Økosamfund, abbreviated LØS) Gaia Villages, Skyumvej 101, DK-7752 Snedsted. *Founded in 1993 to represent, support, develop and inform on sustainable communities. The association now consists of 25 communities and about 100 individual members, with focusses ranging between ecological, social and spiritual. The association assists in the establishment of new communities, both urban and rural. It also lobbies for better financing for environmentally friendly housing, and the removal of other barriers to community establishment.*

SJÆLLAND (ZEALAND, COPENHAGEN)

Ecological Village Society (ØLK) Hågendrupvej 6, Torup, DK-3390 Hundested. ℂ 0045 47 98 70 26 Fax 47 92 45 81 *59 adults and 26 children in four of five planned cohousing groups*

designed as an eco-village of 13 hectares. Organic farming, renewable energy (active/passive solar systems, Finnish massstoves, 450kW windmill), water treatment (five composting toilets), local jobs and integration, campsite. Started 1988 after seven years preparation. 65 km NW of Copenhagen. Train to Dyssekilde/Torup. Open membership. Danish name Økologisk Landsbysamfund K/S.

Svanholm Svanholm Gods, DK-4050 Skibby. *A large income-sharing group, in house groups; consensus decision-making; ecological farming. About 75 adults and 60 children.*

JYLLAND (JUTLAND)

Andelssamfundet i Hjortshøj Lollandsgade 52, DK-8000 Århus C. *Hoping to establish a settlement of 500 people by year 2000. Green, spiritual, politics.*

Baungården Hover Kirkevej 49, DK-7100 Vejle. ℂ 0045 7585 3013 Fax 7585 3806 *6 adults, 3 children. Commune started 1985; active in environmental questions and ecological living. Solibo, based at Baungården, is a small engineering company focussing on environmentally correct products and methods. At present we work mainly with solar heating.*

Ottrupgård Ottrupgård 19, DK-9520 Skørping. ℂ 0045 98 39 29 19 *Co-operative village, started 1992. 22 private houses and a communal farmhouse on the edge of the biggest forest in Denmark, with lakes for swimming. Dining hall for 100 people; most people eat together on the first four days of the week. Every 3rd Sunday is joint working-day. Central boiler, augmented by solar power. 38 adults, 27 children.*

FINLAND

Maailmankauppa (World Shop) Snellmaninkatu 25, 00170 Helsinki. ℂ 00358 (9)0 278 1443 *15 adults, mostly young. 3rd World / Eco shop; contact & info centre; started 1981. Produce guide to responsible consuming; promote walking, cycling & public transport. They will send you list of ecological farmers in Finland for the postage cost.*

FRANCE

Réseaux-Espérance 98 Boulevard des Rocs, F-86000 Poitiers. *Network for personal development and grassroots actions: publishes a newsletter every three months; organises quarterly meetings and a one week gathering every summer.*

Ruralis BP23, F-47130 Port-Sainte-Marie. ℂ 0033 53 67 41 42 Fax 53 87 28 93 *New network of rural communities. Setting up a community in Lot-et-Garonne in a little château and other buildings on 88 hectares of agricultural land and woods.*

ILE-DE-FRANCE (75 77 78 91 92 93 94 95)

Accueil-Convention 52 rue Charles Baudelaire, F-93300 Aubervilliers. ℂ 00331 48 34 27 81 *Welcomes people with pscyhological problems.*

L'Arche à Paris 11 rue François Mouthon, F-75015 Paris. ℂ 00331 42 50 06 48 Fax 48 28 71 62 *Ark Community of Jean Vanier. Communal life shared with mentally handicapped adults. 4 living spaces in Paris with 33 handicapped adults. Also a workshop, and move on space. Christian. We believe that each person, handicapped or not, has a unique and mysterious worth.*

Assise 29/31 rue Guesnier, F-95420 St-Gervais. ℂ 00331 34 67 00 39 *Centre of meditation: Zen in the spirit of K.G. Dürkheim and in the Chritian tradition.*

Emmaüs International BP 91, F-94143 Alfortville Cédex. ℂ 00331 48 93 29 50 Fax 43 53 19 26 *Group of communities worldwide that welcome people with difficulties, whatever their age, whatever their past, offering them somewhere to live and work in solidarity with the dispossessed. Since 1951 have gathered raw materials for recycling. Help victims of war and natural disaster by giving immediate material assistance, and by facilitating local & global development.*

L'Orée 12 rue Ambroise Thomas, F-92400 Courbevoie. *23 adults, 25 children. Christian community, with differing levels of investment in communal life. Members live in different houses; many income share. Work includes home education, provision of retreat space, and*

welcoming adults and children with psychological problems. They do not wish visitors at the moment. Address also at Le Moulin, F-89120 Chêne-Arnoult (6 adults, 15 children).

NORMANDIE (14 27 50 61 76)

Communauté de Caulmont F-76400 Froberville. ℂ 0033 3527 3172 Fax 3527 3667 *Ecumenical Christian community.*

BRETAGNE (22 29 35 44 56)

Communauté de la Poterie La Poterie, F-22980 Plélan-le-Petit. *10 adults, 18 children: five families in five houses. We all work outside. We want to live together according to Christian values.*

POITOU-CHARENTES-VENDÉE (16 17 79 85 86)

La Sepaye Maison d'Accueil Chatenay, F-79150 Moutiers sous Argenton. ℂ 0033 49 65 91 31 *Welcome and support for physically handicapped adults.*

CHAMPAGNE-ALSACE-LORRAINE (08 10 51 52 54 55 57 67 68 88)

Communauté de Bois Gérard F-10130 Chessy-les-Prés. ℂ 0033 25 70 67 09 *Recently established commune in the Burgundy countryside. About 10 adults & 10 children. We try to simplify our lifestyle, to reduce our needs, to share and educate in a spirit of non-violence. We pay particular attention to respecting the environment and human differences, work sharing, minimising waste and eliminating over-consumption. Welcome!*

Ecolonie: Centre Ecologique International Thietry, F-88260 Hennezel. ℂ 0033 29 07 00 27, *10 workers, 7 residents. 30 members. Seeking simple, self-sufficient lifestyle without waste of natural resources and energy. Agriculture, animals, projects for alternative energy. Information weekends the second weekend each month; twice a year for a week an "ecological carrousel" putting ecology into practice; workshops over the summer, and permaculture courses. Please send international reply coupon.*

BOURGOGNE-FRANCHE-COMTÉ (21 25 39 58 70 71 89 90)

Ferme Accueil Visargent, F-71330 Sens-

sur-Seille. *Spirit of Ark Communities.*
8 adults, 16 children: four families living
separately, sharing certain activities and
services. Possibility of pursuing a very
diverse agriculture, and an alternative
way of life in general. Visitors are invit-
ed to share in the life and work of the
farmhouse in return for food and bed.
Have set up an association called Les
Sept Couleurs to further communal spir-
it; planning to build a collective space.

RHONE-ALPES (01 07 26 38 42 69 73 74)
Communauté du Surgeon 9-11 allée des
Cardons, F-69120 Vaulx-en-Velin.
✆ 0033 78 79 16 70 or 78 80 88 23.
Christian community in Lyon suburbs,
founded 1970. Network of over 40 peo-
ple, adults and children, with two
communal houses: La Colombe et
l'Olivier at above address, and the
Communauté de St-Fons at 11 rue René
Fernandez, F-69190 St-Fons. The com-
munity welcomes people in difficulty:
unemployment, alcoholism, rejection,
violence, handicap. "Justice, the right to
be different, care for those who suffer,
for the dispossessed; co-responsibility, a
place for everyone, freedom and solidar-
ity."

Terre et Ciel Le Casage, F-26560
Eygalayes. *Steiner based: biodynamic*
farming, education, therapy, arts and
crafts, caring for people with learning
difficulties. School and holiday place,
especially for children. Experimentation
with new social forms that make possi-
ble the creation and maintenance of
durable agriculture.

MIDI-PYRÉNÉES (09 12 31 32 46 65 81 82)
Bazian F-32230 Louslitges. ✆ 0033 62 70
95 13 Fax 62 70 95 41 *33 adults, 8 chil-*
dren. Loving-Living Place: département
GERS between Toulouse and the
Atlantic Ocean above Pyrénées; 48
hectares, several valleys, own lake,
woods, vineyard, bought 1994 by 33
GERmanS. Vision: International com-
munity living totally truth, honesty, love,
spiritual self-awareness, committed to
consciousness growth, awakening (own)
human potentials; inspired by Paul

Lowe; vegetarian (raw) food; NO
DRUGS!
Le Cun du Larzac route de St-Martin,
F-12100 Millau. ✆ 0033 65 60 62 33
Fax 65 61 33 26 *10 adults, 9 children.*
Experiment for "living and working dif-
ferently" with a non-violent perspective.
Le Cun is also a conference centre fed by
renewable energy (water, wind, sun) and
a research and education centre on con-
flicts and their transformation.
Le Milles Pattes BP 96, F-09200 St-Girons.
✆ 0033 61 66 02 07 *Formed 1987, restor-*
ing a château. Creating a meeting place
where every difference can be expressed,
a place of exchanges, creation and
recreation, of opening to the world. An
art of living, learning beauty, developing
the imaginary. Site of Ecotopia 93, a fes-
tival of European Young Forest Action
(BP 566, NL-6130 AN Sittard).
Mother Earth Land ("Mela") Domaine La Lix,
F-32260 Tachoires. ✆ 0033 62 65 35 04
Fax 62 65 35 92, *40 adults. New age,*
holistic, green, arts and crafts, garden-
ing, farming, macrobiotic vegan food,
free alternative school, various living
groups, 150ha, visitor centre, healing
house, study house.

LANGUEDOC-ROUSSILLON (11 30 34 48 66)
Les Amis de la Douceur et de l'Harmonie El-
Faïtg, F-66230 Serralongue. ✆ 0033 68
39 62 56, *5 adults and 2 children living*
850m above sea level in the charm of the
Pyrénées Orientales, with 21ha of gar-
den and surrounding
forest/mountainside, our community is
vegetarian and spiritual. We have a
vision of a harmonious, gentle world,
where love reigns, and all beings live
peacefully together.
Le Coral F-30470 Aimargues. ✆ 0033 66
88 00 12 Fax 66 88 57 44, *15 people: a*
community welcoming young people
with psychological problems. Students
studying psychology or social work may
come and be part of the community for
one to three months. They organise a
network of other such "Lieux-de-Vie".
Books by Claude Sigala: Visiblement, je
vous aime and Multiplicités. Please ask

for leaflet. Also film in 95 called Visiblement, je vous aime: fiction filmed at Le Coral by Jean-Michel Carré.

Permaculture Pyrénées F-11300 Bouriège. *Voluntary simplicity, sustainable small ecological farm. We welcome apprentices to help with production of cereals using the Bonfils method, growing vegetables the synergistic way, making cheese, bread. Free-range poultry, etc...*

PROVENCE-ALPES-COTE-D'AZUR
(04 05 06 13 83 84)

Longo Mai BP 42, F-04300 Forcalquier. ☎ 0033 92 73 05 98 Fax 92 73 18 18 *Started in 1973, with 30 people settling on 300 hectares on an abandoned mountainside in Provence. Now has over 150 active members and runs Radio Zinzine, a 24 hour free radio station, a visitors village and a music group. Co-operative living and working; Co-founded CEDRI (European committee for the defence of refugees and immigrants), FERL(the European Federation of Community Radios) and the European Civic Forum which seeks to develop links of friendship and co-operation between eastern and western Europe Has established a farming co-op for refugees in Costa Rica. Now has five co-operatives in France: a wool spinning mill near Briançon and four farms, including one near St-Martin-de-Crau, east of Arles, called Mas de Granier: a community and organic vegeta There is a co-op in Switzerland and in Austria. A new co-operative farm was being launched in 1995 in Mecklenburg (NE Germany); various projects have been developed in Transcarpathia (Ukraine).*

GERMANY

Eurotopia Hasenhof 8, D-71540 Murrhardt. ☎ 0049 (0)7192 3218 *Quarterly magazine in German about communal living, and an annual directory of communal groups in Europe (and some outside Europe), with longer listings than we are able to give. They also include embryonic groups. Very useful.*

Ökodorf-Institut Ginsterweg 3, D-31595 Steyerberg. ☎ 0049 (0)5764 2754

Seminars and advice for people wishing to join or set up a community. In our archives are lots of addresses of communities which don't want to be registered in an address list. It's best to visit us in our community, Lebensgarten Steyerberg (see Niedersachsen). Otherwise we will send you a questionnaire for long-distance consultation. Please enclose two international reply coupons from your post office. Mail order service for books about all aspects of community living.

BERLIN

Synanon Bernburgerstraße 10, D-10963 Berlin (Kreuzburg). ☎ 0049 (0)30 250001-0 Fax 250001-73 *Self-help community, founded 1971 by addicts for addicts. Open to every user who is prepared to quit their addiction. Open 24 hours, recommend stay of at least two years. 500 adults and their children live communally in Berlin, Brandenburg and Hessen. Three rules: no drugs, alcohol or other addictive substances; no violence or threat thereof; no smoking. Have a removal and transport business, a printshop and pottery in Berlin, and a pottery and biodynamic farming and gardening in Hessen.*

Ufa-Fabrik Viktoriastraße 13-18, D-12105 Berlin. ☎ 0049 (0)30 755 030 *35 adults, 15 children. Founded 1979 on the site of the former UFA film studios. We run an international culture centre, two theatre halls, the UFA-Circus, a circus school, the samba band Terra Brasilis, workshops for sport, music, dance and theatre, a community centre, children's farm, wholemeal bakery, organic shop, various ecological projects, a free school, café, guesthouse, & much more!*

BRANDENBURG (REGION AROUND BERLIN)

ÖkoLea Hohensteiner Weg 3, D-15345 Klosterdorf.. E-mail: t.crawford@ tbx-2.berliner.in-berlin.de (personal) *16 adults & 6 children sharing living and working space on former dairy farm. Main projects: ecologically sound building, water & energy conservation and organic gardening. Goals include consensus decision-making, communal*

finances and integration in the surrounding community through social service projects. More people welcome.
ZEGG: Centre for Experimental Cultural Design Rosa Luxemburg Strasse 39, D-14806 Belzig. ✆ 0049 (0)33841 59530 Fax 59512 E-mail: kastor@zegg.dinoco.de *50 adults, 17 children. Personal growth / spiritual ecology, new technology, community building, free love without jealousy or competition. Part of the Project Meiga Network which is setting up communities in various places, including Portugal. Projects at Zegg include the Free University, publishing house, ZEGG Magazine, children's project, ecological energy, resonance technology, organic gardening, water and cleansing processes, dolphin research using sound and music. Working to establish a world free of fear, violence and sexual repression.*

SACHSEN (DRESDEN)

Frohberg Schönnewitz 9, D-01665 Krögis b. Meissen. ✆ 0049 (0)35244 41803 Fax (0)35244 41804 *6 adults, 2 children. Organic gardening, natural energy, landscape shaping. Undogmatic spiritual. Seminar house, soft tourism, workshops for wood, electricity and metal.*
Johannishöhe D-01737 Tharandt.. *5 adults. Restoration of buildings probably finished June 95. 7 goats, 5 sheep, many ideas. Links between town and country supported by the "Grüne Liga" Dresden: use for seminars, workcamps, children's summer camps. Open to everyone.*
Lebensgut Pommritz nr 1, D-02627 Pommritz. ✆ 0049 (0)35939 385 *Green, garden/farm, crafts, technology, creativity. 30 adults and 20 children aim for self-sufficiency on 100 hectares. Supported by the regional government.*

MECKLENBURG-VORPOMMERN (ROSTOCK)

Czar Nekla the First D-17121 Zarnekla 19. *6 adults, 5 children. Ecology, therapy, self-sufficiency, gardening / farming. Our common vision: to make a green, blossoming land with free and conscious human beings, where love can grow. You can visit us at any time. The railway station Düvier is nearby. Started*

1992, hoping to grow to 20-30 members.
Feuerlandkommune Ausbau 13, D-17495 Brüssow. ✆ 0049 (0)30 693 2507 *7 adults. Anarchical, crafts & agriculture, work therapy self-help groups. Looking especially for women to join our community. At least 20 people could live here!*

SCHLESWIG-HOLSTEIN (N OF HAMBURG)

Schöpferisches Zentrum OASE Schaarweg 70, D-23730 Neustadt-Rettin. ✆ 0049 (0)4561 7471 or 7358 *16 members from the inner circle; all together we are 60. For people who no longer seek outwards, but are looking to their own inner selves.*

NIEDERSACHSEN (BREMEN, HANNOVER)

Lebensgarten Steyerberg Ginsterweg 3, D-31595 Steyerberg. ✆ 0049 (0)5764 2370 *85 adults, 45 children.Spiritual and ecological focus (Findhorn orientated); permaculture field/forest, bakery, healing centre, art and sound workshop, textile workshop. Founded 1985. See Ökodorf-Institut at start of Germany listing.*
Kommune Niederkaufungen Kirchweg 1, D-34260 Kaufungen. ✆ 0049 (0)5605 80070 Fax (0)5605 800740 *46 adults, 16 children. Building, carpentery, mechanics, seminar house, kindergarten, architecture, leather clothes, catering, organic veg, cattle. Socialist, income-sharing; consensus decisions; communal education, anti-hierarchy, ecologically-sound products, collective work structures & living groups.*
Osho-Stadt-Kommune Stückhauserstraße 39, D-26939 Ovelgönne. ✆ 0049 (0)4480 1661 Fax (0)4480 1624 *Currently small community focussed on Osho spirituality. Plans underway to move to a much larger site in the former DDR to make a community of 500-1000 people, or more. At same address in Ovelgönne is Kristall-Heilungs-Zentrum, a spiritual healing centre that can be hired by groups.*
PrinzHöfte Simmershauserstraße 1, D-27243 Prinzhöfte. ✆ 0049 (0)4244 644 Fax (0)4244 8679 *Centre for Ecological Questions and Holistic Learning. We are 12-15 residents and a few more who don't live here, but regularly come to help. Our subjects are permaculture,*

architecture, alternative energy, Freinet-teaching. We run seminars, and our rooms can also be rented by groups. Visitors welcome; please call in advance.

Troubadour Märchenzentrum Bretthorststraße 140, D-32602 Vlotho. ℂ 0049 (0)5733 10801 Fax 18634 *10 adults, 15 children. Specialise in healing with fairy-tales.*

VERbunt c/o Verdener Umweltwerkstatt,, Herrlichkeit 1, D-27283 Verden/Aller. ℂ 0049 (0)4231 81046 Fax (0)4231 81048 *25 adults, 2 children. A new & growing network of living communities, coopera-tives & political initiatives in Verden near Bremen. We are committed to an environmental organisation, an alterna-tive culture-club, an organic food co-op, an environmental institute, a self-help bikeshop and an organic greengrocer.*

NORDRHEIN-WESTFALEN (KÖLN, DORTMUND)

Lernwerkstatt für neue Lebens- & Arbeitsformen Brunnenstraße 1, D-54570 Niederstadtfeld. ℂ 0049 (0)6596 551 Fax (0)6596 1282 *18 adults, 14 children. Eco-spirituality, eco-politics, feminism, therapy and creativity. We do not live in one building but in individual flats and houses in our village. We've a common centre where we meet. We run a conference centre.*

Mutter Erde Holperstraße 1, D-57537 Forst-Seifen. ℂ 0049 (0)2742 8251 and fax *9 adults, 11 children. Founded 1983, inspired by Paramahansa Yogananda, an inter-faith community of people seek-ing personal development, and aiming for truth, simplicity and love.. Looking for the eternal in the transitory, the unity of creator and created and the fusion of people's material and spiritual selves. Several houses in and around Seifen in beautiful countryside.*

HESSEN (FRANKFURT, KASSEL)

Ökologisch-baubiologische Siedlung Auf dem Heckenstück, D-35075 Gladenbach-Friebertshausen. ℂ 0049 (0)6462 5090 *Ecological settlement using ecological and natural organic materials for house-construction, a flower purification plant for the sewage, meadows with spread traditional types of fruit trees, ponds, etc. The inhabitants agree to being a*

community of neighbours - economically independent. 13 of 18 planned houses are built and lived in. Good for families with young children - 34 already there.

Projektwerkstatt Ludwigstraße 11, D-35447 Reiskirchen-Saasen. ℂ 0049 (0)6401 5651 *4 adults, 1 child. Planning much bigger project, including environmental projects, such as a radio station, a work-shop for making newspapers and a lab for testing water quality. Green, politics, arts, gardening / farming, solar energy.*

RHEINLAND-PFALZ (MAINZ, KOBLENZ)

Dörrwies - Sozialpolitisches Projekt D-54497 Morbach-Merscheid. ℂ 0049 (0)6533 93730 Fax (0)6533 3105 *We are 15-20 children, adults and so-called "mental-ly-handicapped" people. We do gardening, farming (sheep & pigs) and a lot of other things. We have wool prod-ucts, a book and wine shop, a holiday house in Burgundy, France, and one next door to us. We believe in "no gods, no masters" and try to live accordingly. Admin address: Birkenfelderstraße 13; living and working address: Dörrwiese 4.*

Ökologie- und Technologie-Betriebe Eduard-Mann-Straße 1-7, D-67280 Ebertsheim/Pfalz. ℂ 0049 (0)6359 3498 *25 adults and 18 children living in former paper mill and 50,000 m² of land, with differ-ing and financially independent setups. Various individually run enterprises.*

BADEN-WÜRTTEMBERG (STUTTGART, BLACK FOREST)

Communitas Agnus Dei Kloster Frauenberg, D-78351 Bodman-Ludwigshafen. ℂ 0049 (0)7773 5836 or 7490 Fax (0)7773 5805 or 7490 *29 adults, 25 children. Founded 1980: 3 places in Germany and Belgium; also starting a community in Ecuador. We are trying to live a simple and spiri-tual life, following Christ. Prayer and sacramental life is the foundation of our various activities: farming & gardening, different kinds of music, working with pregnant women and damaged people. In Belgium we have a little school: Ecole Don Bosco. We are interested in working together for a "culture of love".*

Doernach D-72218 Wildberg. ℂ 0049

(0)7054 7522 (Saturdays) *8 adults.
BioVersity - Nature Workshop. We play
basic and applied R&D. One of our
focusses is Biotecture with green roofs,
green façades, edible habitat, edible
communities. We plant 1000 trees/year.
Booklist on request, including self-build
book* Natürlich Bauen *by Rudolf Doernach.
Visitors by appointment only please.*
Lebenshaus Maltererstraße 26, D-79102
Freiburg.. *Ecumenical community; shelter & help for people in crisis situations.*
Wasserschlosz Lohrbach D-74821 Mosbach.
✆ 0049 (0)6261 17359 Fax (0)6261
15273 *Old water castle. 8 people born
1953-1912 in 4 living groups; 7 more
flats between 70 and 250m² ready or
under construction, offered for buying.
Want to end the separation of living,
working and free time. Much of their 2.6
hectares set aside as ecological wetland.*

BAYERN / BAVARIA

Connection Medien GmbH Hauptstraße 5, D-
84494 Niedertaufkirchen. ✆ 0049
(0)8639 6009-0 Fax (0)8639 1219
*14 adults, 6 children. Spirituality, thera-
py, green, politics. Publishers of
Connection magazine, people centre.*
Projekt Eulenspiegel Modell Wasserburg
e.V., Gasthof Zum Eulenspiegel,
Dorfstraße 25, D-88142 Wasserburg/
Bodensee. ✆ 0049 (0)8382 887875
*7 adults & 3 children run an ecological-
ly-orientated inn (a cultural centre with
a guesthouse) and produce newsletter*
Jedermensch. *Community development
and day-to-day planning happen at two
communal breakfasts. Some of us practise
political anthroposophy. Founded 1976.*
Schäfereigenossenschaft Finkhof St Ulrich-
straße 1, D-88410 Arnach/Bad Wurzach.
✆ 0049 (0)7564 931730 *Since 1979 with
fluctuating membership, several work
areas: sheep farming, wool mail-order
business, office for environmental
advice, and more. No spiritual ideology.*
Stamm Füssen Eins Magnusplatz 6, D-87629
Füssen. ✆ 0049 (0)8362 38993 *40 adults,
43 children. Green, politics, spiritual,
arts/crafts, therapy, gardening, technology.*

GREECE

Harmonious Living contact address: Robert
Najemy, Harmonious Living, Griva 29,
Halandri 152 33, Athens. ✆ 0030 681 8151
Retreat & seminar centre near Athens.
New Humanity Centre Eleonon Road,
Akroyali Avias, Kalamata 24100.
*Aquarian esoteric wisdom centre dedi-
cated to holistic service to humanity and
the hierarchy. Publishes quarterly*
Enhumanity. *Seminar space available.
Aspiring, selfless and self-supporting
esoteric wisdom teachers and co-opera-
tive lightworkers are welcome to apply
in person for needed voluntary service to
build a model new humanity World
Golden Age Community. Attempting to
set up a provisional world parliament.*

HUNGARY

Gyürüfü Alapítvány Arany János u. 16, H-
7935 Ibafa. ✆ 0036 73 354 334 Fax 354
107 E-mail bela@borsos.zpok.hu or
gyurufu.zpok.hu *20 adults, ecological
village community: crafts, farming,
gardening, technology, sustainable rural
environmental planning.*

IRELAND

NORTHERN IRELAND

Columbanus Community of Reconciliation 683
Antrim Road, Belfast BT15 4EG ✆ 0044
(0)1232 778009 (01232 778009 from UK)
*Founded 1983, 6 adults. Fully residen-
tial community of men and women, lay
and clerical, of different Christian traditions, Protestant, Anglican and Catholic.
The Community usually about six in
number, seeks to live out the values of
Christian unity, justice and peace in a
spirit of reconciliation and to share its
vision with others. To this end it helps to
service the works of other agencies, secular and religious; it sponsors a youth
project and an inter-school community
relations project. It provides the premises and the ethos in which small groups
of Christians of different backgrounds
can come together for meetings, for quiet
days of prayer and for talks. New members are welcome for a period of a year
or more. Members share goods, time and
talents and make a weekly contribution*

towards their keep; visitors also pay according to their means. The is communal prayer, both morning and evening; members come together for a daily meal and for other organised functions. The Community is self-governing and has a weekly community meeting; it is, at the same time, accountable to its Patrons and Trustees. More detailed information is available on enquiry.

REPUBLIC OF IRELAND

Atlantis / An Droichead Beo Burtonport, Co. Donegal. ✆ *00353 (0)75 42030 Alternative therapy centre and youth hostel. An Droichead Beo is a large 18 roomed house, run by 4 young people. We're all involved with Atlantis but at present we're a stepping stone or contact point for the main group that has emigrated to South America. We're into alternative healing, crafts, magic, practical things like carpentry, building, gardening & decorating. Plenty of room here for emotional expansion, and plenty of enjoyable, creative hard work. Also open as a hostel for travellers. If interested, write or phone, or just turn up. As we are just starting out and our garden has yet to grow we would greatly appreciate any financial contributions that could be made. Hope to hear from you soon. P.S. We are also non-smoking.*

Inisglas Trust Crossabeg, Co. Wexford.

Bio-dynamic farming community. Our aim is to act as a centre for the study and practice of the bio-dynamic approach to working with the land and community living. 13 adults, 5 children.

Meitheal Inch Island, Co. Donegal. ✆ *00353 (0)77 60323 Working retreat / spiritual community, meditation, organic garden. Children friendly. Inspired by Findhorn. Practical spirituality and group work. Family summer camps and guest programme. Vegetarian, non smoking.*

Comune di Bagnaia podere Bagnaia, fraz. Ancaiano, I-53018 Sovicille, Siena. ✆ 0039 (0)577 311014 *15 adults, 2 children. Income sharing organic farming community. Founded 1979; raise animals, tend pastures, cereal crops, vegetable garden, vines and olive trees; whole economy is held in common. Would welcome visitors, a few at a time, from other communities, to exchange experiences and hospitality.*

Fondazione Bhole Baba Casella Postale 138, I-72014 Cisternino (Brindisi). *Very spiritual, simple and harmonious, situated in a beautiful area in south Italy. Indian-influenced guru ashram. Their guru is Babaji, Herakhan Baba. Permanent sacred fire (dhuni) and temple: arati morning and evening. The ashram started in 1979, willed by Shri Babaji.*

Damanhur via Pramarzo 3, I-10080 Baldissero Canavese, Torino. ✆ 0039 (0)124 512226 Fax (0)124 512150 *Born in 1975; today has over 400 inhabitants and over 15,000 supporters. Damanhur is an innovative way of living. Spread out over the valley of Valchiusella. Oberto Airaudi is inpirator and guide. Life conceived as a constant meditation. The search for full awareness in each activity creates a way of life in which every action aims at contacting the soul and at promoting collective spiritual growth. Art and aesthetic research are fundamental aspects for the growth of Damanhur's society; play makes possible new visions of reality and overcoming attachment to habits and the fruit of the action. Celebrate solstices and equinoxes, and annual day of con-*

tact with the dead. *Underground Temple of Mankind. Guided visits to community offered if booked in advance.*
Passalmonte Campagna 52, I-06065 Passignano (Perúgia). ✆ 0039 (0)75 826563 *German-italian community of 6 adults and 4 children: arts & crafts, horses. Soft tourism: walking and cycling tours. Italian language courses and childrens holidays. Creating an ecology centre "PANTA REI" with other communities. Founded 1984.*
Rainbow Eco Peace Village Italia Cheggio, I-28030 Viganella, Novara. ✆ 0039 (0)324 56315 and fax. *12 adults, 6 children. Established community as an interim while planning the rainbow eco-village. Permaculture, spiritual, arts, technology, politics. Yoga centre. Peace & Eco-Institute. Focalizer for European Rainbow Gathering. Visitors and volunteers welcome. Solar energy projects. Looking for donations to help in rebuilding of village.*
Utopiaggia Villa Piaggia 21, I-05010 Montegabbione (Terni). ✆ 0039 (0)763 87020 *We are an anarchic humanitarian commune, living as ecologically as possible with the land. Community started in Bavaria in 1975; moved to Italy 1982. Many of the founding members came out of the sixties movement. 20 adults and 15 adolescents and children living in 3 houses on 100 hectares of hillside land. Large flock of sheep provides basis for commercial cheese production. Pottery, other handicrafts, language courses (Italian, German, English). Openings for new members. Visitors are always welcomed, but should first write.*

NETHERLANDS

Earth Village Network Postbus 1179, NL-1000 BD Amsterdam. E-mail: earthvill@communication.nl Web site: http:\\intouch.info.nl\EVNhome.htm *International foundation aiming to create durable permaculture communities. Plans to acquire land in different places on the planet, and hold it thereafter in common. Group of 16 people meet regularly in Amsterdam. Planning a support network and information resource. This info has come from Permaculture*

Pyrénées in France. English contact: Persh Hannah Sassoon, 18 Lillington Road, Leamington Spa CV32 5YY, UK. *Tel: 0044 (0)1926 424480.*
Landelijke Vereniging Centraal Wonen Grenadadreef 1-J, NL-3563 HE Utrecht. ✆ 0031 (0)30 612585 *National association of co-housing projects. Housing co-ops with communal facilities.*
De Hobbitstee van Zijlweg 3, NL-8351 HW Wapserveen.. *8 adults, 7 children. Founded 1969, the oldest community in Holland. Rural, self-supporting, income-sharing. Main focus: ecology, non-violence, spirituality, personal growth.*
The Humaniversity Dr Wiardi Beckmanlaan 4, NL-1931 BW Egmond-aan-Zee. ✆ 0031 (0)72 5064114 Fax 5061844 *Founded 1978 by Swami Anand Veeresh and Samadhi-Mariet Wijnen. In addition to an intensive residential program, we offer weekend groups, workshops, courses and therapist training. Important aspects of Humaniversity Therapy are human contact, emotional release, sexuality and meditation. The learning process is based on direct experience. It is deep break-through work that requires strong motivation from the participants.*
De Warkstee Spoorlaan 31, NL-9774 PC Adorp. ✆ 0031 (0)5909 1411 *Living and working co-op, started 1974. Aims to be a warm, lively, active centre for reflection and growth. The community seeks old and new spiritual connections and aims to bring a holistic, new-age co-operative form to everyday life. Holds workshops. Please write for a list.*

NORWAY

Vidaråsen Landsby 3240 Andebu. ✆ 0047 33 44 41 00 Fax 33 44 01 91 *A Camphill Village Community; about 150 people in 17 households. The village was founded in 1966; has a biodynamic farm and garden and various craft workshops.*

POLAND

Gdansk Zen Centre ul. Kartuska 278a, 80-125 Gdansk.
Kraków Zen Centre ul. Smolki 14/1, 30-503 Kraków.

Kuan Um School of Zen ul. Malowiejska 22/24, 04-962 Warszawa. ✆ 0048 2 15-05-52 (office, day only); 15-04-00 (head temple) Fax 15-05-52 (office) E-mail KuanUm@gate.maloka.waw.pl *Daily Zen practice. 3 month winter retreat. 3 week summer retreat. Resident teacher.*

SPAIN

Associación Arte Elemental Calle Merced 33, E-11391 Facinas (Cádiz). ✆ 0034 (9)56 687044 Fax (9)56 687293 *12 adults. On mountainside, close to beaches, 'shop window' permaculture project open daily to public April-Sept, weekends only Oct-March. Solar and wind energy, compost toilets, natural foods kitchen. Also art gallery, craft workshops & shop, music and performance space. 20 eco-hand-crafted chalets planned for rural tourism. Visitors work 30 hours a week & contribute nominal fee. All welcome, but Spanish speakers have more fun.*

Palma Zen Centre C/ Sant Feliu 6, E-07012 Palma de Mallorca. ✆ 0034 (9)71 728981 *Meditation centre of the Kuam Um School of Zen, under the direction of Zen Master Seung Sahn, 78th patriarch from the Buddha and Zen master in the Chogye order of Korean Buddhism. Offer traditional Buddhist meditation every week, & 2 intensive retreats every year.*

SWEDEN

Iskcon Korsnäs Gard, S-14792 Grödinge. *40 adults, some children. Hare Krishna community in an old manor, surrounded by hills and lakes. "Up here we have a farm community, school for children, a few restaurants, sawmill, some shops, Food for Life programme, preaching centres, cooking courses, and most of all, we are publishing the old Vedic literature in different languages.*

Kursgården Lindsberg Lindsberg 10, S-79191 Falun. *10 adults. A course-centre outside Falun. Originates from and inspired by environmental, peace and solidarity movements. The course-centre is managed by a community (10 adults), who try to live by natural resources. We use renewable energy resources as firewood and solar energy.*

Solicentrum Box 16, S-28072 Killeberg. ✆ 0046 (0)479 30580 or 30515 *A Linbu community. Principles for society formulated in The Theory of Conscious Light by H. Linbu, who actively leads the community. Practical application of esoteric wisdom. "We welcome all with good will, sincerity and a wish to work with us. We try to realise our dreams and for that we need to dig deep to gather!"*

Stjärnsund Stiftelsen Stjärnsund, S-77070 Långshyttan. ✆ 0046 (0)225 80001 or 80210 Fax 80301 *Findhorn-inspired community in beautiful surroundings with fairly loose membership structure. Residential courses all the year, working guest programme. Families welcome, hectic during the summer!*

SWITZERLAND

Karthago Postfach 406, CH-8026 Zürich. *Karthago is a model for communal living based on the ideas of p.m.'s bolo'bolo. Three generations, a lot of kids and some ateliers under one roof, strong ties with agriculture and a communal kitchen are the features. In Spring 95 they bought a four storey building in central Zürich. They are scheduled to move in after some renovation in 1996. Please contact via the Paranoia City bookshop at the postbox address given. Note that the shop was due to move to Bäckerstrasse 9 in June 95.*

Kraftwerk 1 Postfach 406, CH-8026 Zürich. *A village in the city of Zürich for 700 people. Experimental architecture meets ecology. Another offspring from bolo'bolo. Contact via the Paranoia City bookshop at the postbox address given.*

Hofgemeinschaft Waldenstein CH-4229 Beinwil (SO). ✆ 0041 (0)61 791 9328 *'Love as a direction and answer for the Earth. Holistic living alternatives as solutions to present and future problems.' Our Holistic Culture Foundation and the Waldenstein village community aims to recognise, try out and rework these ideas. Life school of holistic culture and a community: eco-village and settlement, family, cells for new living.*

LATIN AMERICA

COLOMBIA

Atlantis Contact address: Rebecca Garcia, Lista de Correos, Telecom, Tolima. *10 adults, 7 children. A noisy self-expressive hard-working group, matriarchal in the sense that pleasure, feelings, atmosphere, non-superficial communication and a well-stocked kitchen come first. We grow coffee, sugar-cane, corn, bananas, European veg and South American crops; we are trying to buy chain-saw threatened forest around them. Visitors welcome.*

AUSTRALASIA

AUSTRALIA

SOUTH AUSTRALIA

Cennednyss Community P.O. Summertown, SA 5141. E-mail: dlg@malurus.dialix. oz.au *10 adults, 7 children. Five houses and 15 acres in the Adelaide Hills. Started 1978. Rural, but 15 km from G.P.O. Adelaide. Information about other communities in Australia.*

QUEENSLAND

Crystal Waters Permaculture Village Contact address: Max Lindegger, 56 Isabella Ave, Nambour Qld 4560. ✆ 0061 (0)74 944 622 or 566 or 620 (co-op) *100 adults, 55 children. World's first permaculture village. Designed for about 250 residents, established in present form 1988. Article D&D 94/95. 83 residential lots; predominance of families; 15 single-person households. Adults mostly aged 30-45. Variety of dwellings: timber, pole-frame, brick, mud-brick and pisé. Co-op exists to benefit its members financially & socially, and manages the leasehold lots, visitors' camping area, the Village, Community House & Carousel. The Village planned as commercial centre of community. Please ring to arrange visits and courses.*

Mandala MS 394 via Warwick, Qld 4370.. *Established in 1975, this secular, rural community with about 30 diverse residents is moving towards intentionality by running environmental and community education programs, sharing more resources, and working on our relation-ships. Our lives are full and exciting. Positive visitors welcome. Please write first. See article in this edition.*

NEW SOUTH WALES

Christians Box A678, Sydney Sth, NSW 2000. E-mail: miald@newcastle.edu.au *25 adults in Australia and India. Live communally, share all possessions. In Madras work in thatch slum cleaning toilets and sewers, educating kids, first-aid clinic and sports. Inspired by Gandhian ideals and practical appplication of the Teachings of Christ. In Australia demonstrations against greed and religious hypocrisy. Workers welcome.*

Ferndale c/o Uki P.O., via Murwillumbah, NSW 2484. *Formed 1976, 74 hectares in the far NE corner of New South Wales: sub-tropical rainforest with some pastured areas. 11 homesites. Monthly meetings of the co-op that owns land. Members lead own lives. but from time to time share common interests, friendships and meet for social events at our community shed. Grew from a common desire to live rurally in affordable housing. No structured activities; our work days are erratic. Any visitors usually camp on our common land. No domestic cats or dogs. Average age 40.2 years.*

Yurt Farm The Living & Learning Centre, Graben Gullen Rd, Goulburn, NSW 2580. ✆ 0061 (0)48 292 114 or (0)18 483 960 (mobile) *Rural, food production, healing, learning to live with less. Visitors welcome to help run farm or children's camp, or to join the co-op. Artistic, agricultural and people skills highly valued.*

AUSTRALIAN CAPITAL TERRITORY

Wyuna Community 24 Morant Circuit, Kambah, ACT 2902, Canberra. ✆ 0061 (0)6 296 2960 *We aim to live as an intentional family, to follow lifestyles chosen by us which provide maximum opportunities for human and spiritual growth. We accept as our starting point the theoretical work of Jim Cairns, whose energy was the catalyst for this project. We aim to research and assess small and more appropriate farming and building techniques, focusing on appropriate* technology and alternative energy sources, and address living alternaties to wage / income dependence and the development of creative leisure in a society where jobs are rapidly disappearing.

VICTORIA

Mount Murrindal Co-op Buchan, Victoria 3885. ℂ 0061 (0)51 550 218 or 225 or 222 5 families; communal gardens and orchards. Personal and spiritual growth on Findhorn model. Craft businesses and headquarters of WWOOF Australia. Visitors by arrangement, paying or wwoofing. WWOOF in Australia is Willing Workers on Organic Farms, and is co-ordinated by Lionel Pollard. See networks section for UK address, who can supply international contacts. Good way of visiting communities.

Ontos Health Retreat Gelantipy Road, Buchan P.O., Victoria 3885. ℂ 0061 (0)51 550 275 Fax 550 277 We are 5 adults and 6 children on a 700 acre organic farm and health retreat, with a visiting population that has exceeded 200 for special events. Visitors welcome as part of the WWOOF program or health retreat guests. Property developed in 1980: yoga, meditation, bushwalking, organic orchards, huge gardens, excellent accommodation and food.

NEW ZEALAND

Centrepoint Community PO Box 35, Albany. ℂ 0064 (0)9 415 9468 Fax 415 8471 Founded in 1978, and is now a leaderless / leaderful community of approx. 100 residents seeking to live an extraordinary balance between intimate, co-operative togetherness and individual development. Rural property of 93 acres, with self-supporting businesses and personal growth workshops.

Renaissance Community Trust Graham Downs Farm, Graham Valley, RD1 Motueka, Nelson. 65 adults & children. Started 1979. Low-key farming (horses, small dairy herd, timber, fruit trees). Currently restructuring organisation and design on Permacultural principles. Involvement with neighbouring

Mountain Valley School (run on Summerhill lines). Several member families are WWOOF Hosts.

Riverside Community RD2 Upper Moutere, Nelson (postal address: property located in Lower Moutere). ℂ 0064 (0)3 5267 805 30 adults, 30 children. Pacifist/spiritual, started 1941. Common economic base - 500 acres, dairy farm, organics, forestry, joinery. Consensus decision-making. 3 shared meals per week. Book about Riverside's history available from them. Hostel for visitors and workers.

Tui Land Trust Wainui Bay, RD1 Takaka, Golden Bay. ℂ 0064 (0)3 525 9654 Fax 525 8659 15 adults, 12 children. Community Village for Holistic Living, founded 1984; Communal Meeting and Ritual Space. Emphasis on human potential and communication development. No common religious / political creed or spiritual leader. Children are communal and parental responsibility. Non-income sharing. Share daily lunch; weekly meetings; frequent meditations, celebrations, etc. Visitors welcome: 1 week minimum; after 2 weeks extension must be asked for in community meeting. As usual contact in advance.

ASIA

INDIA

Atmasantulana Village near MTDC Holiday Resort, Karla 410 405. ℂ 0091 (0)2114 82232 Fax 82230 A holistic spiritual and healing community based on Indian culture and ayurveda. We welcome all those who wish to stay and participate in the community program, which includes yoga, meditation, lectures and cultural events. Healthy vegetarian food; natural ayurvedic therapies for rejuvenation and treatment.

Mitraniketan Community Mitraniketan PO, Vellanad 695 543, Kerala. ℂ 0091 (0)471 82045, 82015 or 82086 About 100 adults and 300 children. Farming, various arts, crafts, schools, publishing, promotion of ecological and environmental development, experience of international living. We have a view to develop Universal or global responsibility among people while working with people at local and national level. Our aim is a holistic approach to promote development. This community is non-sectarian, and non-profit making, open to all irrespective of caste, colour, religion and nationality.

ISRAEL

International Communes Desk (I.C.D.) Yad Tabenkin Study Centre, Efal P.O., Ramat-Efal 52960. Supplies information about kibbutzim in Israel and up-to-date info about communities in 30 countries all round the world. They publish the magazine Call, with international communes news in English. The kibbutz movement started in 1909; today there are 250 secular and 17 religious groups.

PHILIPPINES

IARD - International Association for Rural Development Duchess Pension, Puerto Princesa City, 5300 Palawan.. Forming eco-village. Envisaged projects: rice farm and mill, farming co-op, fishing, self-sufficiency; crafts and trade; tourism; ecological research and advice; chapel, creche, medical care, social services, culture; garden restaurant and disco. Address in Switzerland: Walter Stucki, Ramsi, CH-3421 Lyssach.

THE EDITORS

Chris Coates

Born 1957. Building Animateur, Quantum Mechanic and New Age Heretic. Long term member of People in Common. Enjoys the dance that leads to the goldfish in the eye of the rose.

Jonathan How

Born 1953. A man with more pies than fingers to put in them. Happiest eating breakfast at a Little Chef.

Lee Jones

Born 1940. A founder member of the Quaker Community at Bamford. Having "retired" from social work in her early 5os to do an MA in Peace Studies at Bradford University, she now co-ordinates a community mediation service in Sheffield.

William Morris

Born 1961. Has lived at Lifespan and Ritherdon Road. Compiles the D&D overseas section, and designs and writes the Lunar Tree Calendar. Has tried unsuccessfully to set up a gay men's community and a naturist community since the last edition. E-mail address: william@pavilion.co.uk.

Andy Wood

Born 1957. Here seen through the eyes of Rosie - his 10 year old daughter:

My Dad
Afshan thinks he's a thriller,
I just think he's a gorilla.
Afshan thinks he's so great,
I just think that he's an ape.
Afshan says, or so she sang,
"Your Dad can't be an orang-atang!"
Afshan says that he's so funky,
I just think that he's a monkey.
He taps his fingers on the chair,
he has grown so much hair
you cannot tell if he's really there.

Publications about holistic cultural change ... from the edge of time ...

Edge of Time is a new marketing and distribution co-op which has grown out of D&D. From books about communal living to lunar calendars and guides to ritual. Make cheques payable to "Edge of Time Ltd". Overseas orders add an extra £1 per title, please pay in £ sterling.

From Utopian Dreaming to Communal Reality
£15.50 post paid
Bill Metcalf
UNSW Press
ISBN 0 86840 087 4
196 pp pb, b&w illus.
See review on page 33

Is it Utopia Yet?
£13 post paid
Kat Kinkade   *Twin Oaks Pub.*
ISBN 0 9640445 0 1
320 pp pb, b&w illus.
See review on page 55

SPECIAL OFFER: BACK NUMBERS

Diggers & Dreamers 90/91   £2.50 post paid
ISBN 0 9514945 0 3   128 pp pb, b&w illus.
Diggers & Dreamers 92/93   £3.50 post paid
ISBN 0 9514945 1 1   216 pp pb, b&w illus.
Diggers & Dreamers 94/95   £4 SOLD OUT
ISBN 0 9514945 2 X   220 pp pb, b&w illus.

Featuring over 500 completely updated listings for communities in North America plus 70 in other continents. In addition 31 articles cover various aspects of co-operative living.

Communities Directory
£19.50 post paid
FIC   ISBN 0 9602714 3 0
440 pp pb, b&w illus.

D&D's sister publication.
If you're looking for an unusual break for yourself or searching for places to run courses this is an indispensable guide to all those residential facilities "with a difference".

Places to BE 95/96
£6.50 post paid
Edited by Jonathan How
Coherent Visions
ISBN 0 9524396 0 3
112 pp pb, b&w illus.

catalogues from
PO Box 1808
Winslow
Buckingham
MK18 3RN

Dear Reader

*We hope that you have found **Diggers and Dreamers 96/97** to be both useful and enjoyable. We welcome your feedback and invite you to fill out this postcard and return it to us. No stamp is required.*

What features did you like best about Diggers and Dreamers 96/97?

What features would you add to a future edition?

What features would you leave out of a future edition?

Name

Address

Postcode

❑ *We will continue to mail you about this and other publications distributed by Edge of Time unless you tick this box*

Dear Potential or Existing Community/Housing Co-op

*Not listed in **Diggers and Dreamers 96/97**? Make sure that we know about your co-operative or communal group when we come to compile **Diggers and Dreamers 98/99**.*
Fill out this postcard and return it to us. No stamp is required.

Name of group

Address

Postcode

Telephone number

Contact Name

Describe your group briefly: what it does; whether it exists already or not; etc

PO Box 1808
Winslow
Buckinghamshire
MK18 3BR

BUSINESS REPLY SERVICE
Licence No MK1659

PO Box 1808
Winslow
Buckinghamshire
MK18 3BR